The Natural Landscapes of Canada

A Study in Regional Earth Science

J. Brian Bird

with an introduction
by F. K. Hare

The Natural

A Study in

Landscapes of Canada

Regional Earth Science

Wiley Publishers of Canada Limited

Toronto

Library of Congress Catalog Card
No. 72-000075
ISBN 0-471-07370-9
ISBN 0-471-07371-7

Editorial consultants:
Christine Purden Associates

Printed and bound in Canada by
The Bryant Press Limited for
Wiley Publishers of Canada Limited

Contents

Maps and Diagrams

Plates

Preface

Canada is a large country; within its borders is a range of scenery that matches in variety that of any other country of the world. And yet the disturbing experience of geography teachers in high schools and universities is that to students, and by inference to the population as a whole, the landscapes of Canada remain unknown and unappreciated. Travel across the country, or indeed farther than 150 miles from one's native city, apparently is still rare for Canadians. In the last two decades, however, increased leisure for some and a growing wanderlust in others have led to greater exploration of the country both by Canadians and by their neighbours south of the border.

Perhaps curiosity about the land already exists; but if it does, little written information is available to satisfy and stimulate it. A definitive physiography of Canada has yet to be written. Systematic and regional data are still being collected, sifted, and modified. It may be many years before a major work comparable to the early United States studies of Isaiah Bowman[1] and N. M. Fenneman[2] is written. Nevertheless, great advances in our knowledge of the evolution of the scenery have been made in the past twenty years. This book is the first to describe Canada's major landforms in terms of both the underlying geology and contemporary views of their geomorphological evolution.

Although in the pages that follow Canada's early geology is discussed in general terms, the main emphasis is given to events in roughly the final million years – during the Quaternary. In this final period of the earth's history, the dual cataclysms of the Pleistocene glaciations and the arrival of man – Indian, Eskimo, and European – have modified the physical landscape at a rate that can rarely have been equalled in the more remote geological past. Some sections of the book are based on the published and unpublished research of other geographers, but this material has necessarily been greatly compressed. In some parts I have drawn principally on my own, often unpublished, field observation; and in some areas, we still do not have sufficient knowledge to provide rational generalizations.

The initial concept of the book must be attributed to the late Professor Sir Dudley Stamp, who in the early 1950s produced one with similar objectives on the British Isles.[3] He was a frequent visitor to Canada, and many of his ideas are incorporated here. The book also owes a great deal to Dr. F. K. Hare, who wrote the introduction and who in the early stages planned several of the chapters; Dr. Hare withdrew from full co-authorship only when his other commitments became too great.

A work of this character could be written only with the assistance of many people. Inevitably, several chapters have been compiled from published papers and from discussions with field scientists in all parts of the country. This work is therefore indebted to the many physical geographers and geologists who are working to unravel the story of the Canadian landscape.

---

[1] Isaiah Bowman, *Forest Physiography* (New York: John Wiley & Sons, Inc., 1911).

[2] N. M. Fenneman, *Physiography of Western United States* (New York: McGraw-Hill Book Company, 1931); and by the same author, *Physiography of Eastern United States* (New York: McGraw-Hill Book Company, 1938).

[3] L. Dudley Stamp, *Britain's Structure and Scenery*, 4th ed. (London: Collins, 1955).

The object of the book is to provide an introduction to the scenery of Canada in terms that can be readily understood, but which will not lose their scientific validity as a result of simplification and analogy. It is hoped that the curious traveller will find it interesting and that for students of the geography of Canada and of geomorphology, in advanced high school courses, in colleges, and in universities, it will provide useful examples and explanations seldom found in current standard textbooks.

My thanks are due to the many geomorphologists, geographers, and geologists who have helped, both directly and indirectly, to make this book possible. In particular, I wish to thank Mr. A. Sen for his careful drafting of the diagrams. Acknowledgement is also made to all who have permitted figures to be reproduced from their published work and particularly to A. H. Strahler for Figures 3-1, 3-2, and 13-10; to the Ontario Research Foundation for Figure 3-3; and to the Geological Survey of Canada for permission to reproduce Figure 13-3 and other figures credited to the Survey.

At present, the most complete information on the landscapes of Canada is contained in *Geology and Economic Minerals of Canada* (R. J. W. Douglas (ed.), Geol. Survey Can., 1971, 838 pp.). Inevitably, in a limited study of this type, many questions are left unanswered. The reader who wishes to pursue these questions in greater depth should refer to the Survey book and to a list of selected readings which has been added to each chapter. The literature on the scenery of Canada is limited, however, and there are few parts of the country that are adequately covered by regional monographs. In many areas, additional information can be obtained only from detailed, specialist papers. Consequently, the list of selected readings is short and variable, and includes general works to provide background knowledge, regional accounts when they are available, and occasional reference to some of the more important scientific papers.

Introduction

Canada at Large

Canada is huge—over three and a half million square miles—and encompasses a vast range of landscapes. This book describes these landscapes, and tries to explain their character and origin.

It is, above all, a northern country. The processes that work to carve out its hills and valleys are dominated by this fact. To find them at work elsewhere one must go to Scandinavia, or to parts of the northern U.S.S.R. Finland and Quebec, Norway and British Columbia, are natural pairs. Their affinities are apparent at a glance. And there is an obvious resemblance between the Prairies and the steppes and wheatlands of the Ukraine, as the Ukrainian settlers saw decades ago.

The fact that Canada is big and northern makes Canadians akin to other northern peoples, rather than to the Americans to the south, although their culture does not reflect this kinship. Canadians have not, as a nation, put the North anywhere near the centre of their mythology: they have no Snow Queens to boast about. But they have had to cope with northern conditions, and they have learned how to maintain communications and sovereignty over the most distant parts of their patrimony. Ellesmere Island, the northernmost territory, is at one point barely 400 miles from the pole; Alert, the remotest Arctic weather station, is as far from Montreal as Los Angeles is, and is closer to U.S.S.R. territories than to the populous parts of Canada. Yet the latter—the belt of farms and cities stretching from Victoria to St. John's, Newfoundland, itself as long as the distance from Montreal to the equator—are in the same latitudes as France and the British Isles.

This position is significant in the story of Canada's natural landscapes, for the northern climates have special qualities. They are characterized by great contrasts in temperature between the seasons, and between day and night; and a tremendous amount of snow is deposited annually, lying undisturbed on the winter landscapes for weeks or months. In the Pleistocene period, Canada was the centre of the largest and most powerful ice sheets to cover the land areas of the earth. This, again, Canada shared with Scandinavia, where the other large ice sheets were centred. The geomorphic processes that have gradually sculptured the country's landscapes have thus been very special.

Landforms—the individual units of a landscape—are created by the interaction of climate with rocks on the earth's surface. This interaction proceeds very slowly, so that the youngest landforms are old in human terms. We must observe and examine present landforms with the utmost care to reconstruct correctly the story of their origins. Especially is this true of the structure of the rocks beneath the surface. If landform evolution is slow, the pace at which the rocks of the crust are folded, faulted, or warped is even slower. By far the easiest of these things to observe is the interaction of the climate with soils, vegetation, river systems, and ground water. And in Canada, as we have said, what we see is the northern aspect of this system of interaction.

Canadians hardly need convincing that their climate is close to glacial. No people on earth have a harder winter to complain about, latitude for latitude. Other nations may have difficulty in visualizing what an ice age means. Canadians have none, because they live not far from reality.

Central and eastern Canada are astonishingly cold for their latitudes. In mid-winter, the zero Celsius isotherm for mean air temperature swings far south into the United States. Only in coastal British Columbia, in fact, does the mean temperature stay above freezing. In the Prairie Provinces, Ontario, Quebec, and the Atlantic Provinces, it stays below freezing for 3–6 months in the year, although occasional mid-winter thaws remind us that there are warmer regions from which we can draw a little passing relief. Toronto, Ottawa, and Montreal have severe winters, in which heavy snows alternate with periods of great cold—often below 0°F (−17°C), with fresh winds. Yet these cities are in the latitudes of Bordeaux, the French Riviera, Florence, and Venice, where winter frosts are brief aberrations in an otherwise equable regime. The Prairies, too, have a winter like that of Siberia, rather than that of Britain, in whose latitudes they lie.

Do these cold winters mean that Canada could be once again invaded by continental ice sheets, like the one that still covers Greenland? Or are they relics of the Ice Age just ended? And will matters soon improve?

We cannot answer these questions dogmatically. It is certain, however, that the cold winter climate is a first cousin of the climates of full glacial conditions. The most recent ice to cover eastern Canada—the Laurentide glacier of Wisconsin times—left terminal moraines across the Prairies, the Great Lakes region, and southern Ontario and Quebec whose courses we can easily trace and date. We know where the outer limit of the Wisconsin glacier was located at various dates during its withdrawal. These old pausing-stages of the ice front are roughly parallel to one another. Most strikingly they are also nearly parallel to the winter isotherms of today. The ice plunged farthest south in the Great Lakes area, and 10,000 years ago its southernmost margin was still north of Lake Huron. The present-day winter isotherms have very similar courses. Flying east in April, when the Prairies have already lost their snow cover, one sees the still frozen and snow-laden surfaces of eastern Canada almost exactly where glacial ice lay 12,500 years ago.

What causes this great winter cold? It is certainly not a lack of solar radiation. In this respect, Canada's climate is more abundant than normal. If we take as a criterion the net radiation income per annum (absorbed solar radiation less the net radiative cooling of the surface), then southern Canada's income is comparable with that of Spain, Italy, and Greece. About 40 kilocalories of energy are received annually per square centimeter of surface in a broad belt from the Straits of Georgia across to the Montreal Plain, equivalent to a little over 50 watts per square meter. Since the great winter cold cannot be due to a local energy lack, it must be imported. It arrives, in fact, in wave after wave of cold outblowing airstreams from the high Arctic, which find the open surface of central North America an easy southward route. These cold waves are Canada's winter monsoon, comparable in origin with the Asian winter monsoon. The people of China and Japan also experience harsh winters brought by northerly winds from a frozen continent.

Canada is saved from glaciation by the warmth of summer, which is spectacularly different from winter. In winter and spring, great quantities of snow accumulate on the upper slopes of the western mountains and over a vast area of central and eastern Canada. In late spring, the sun warms the Arctic and cuts off the southward flow of arctic air. Long hours of brilliant sunshine in May and June remove the snow even from the high plateaus of Labrador–Ungava, though a few patches survive most summers on the higher ground and a few tiny glacierettes occupy shaded cirques in the Torngat Mountains. But the crucial point is that there is enough energy, every year, to chase the snow away from the entire land area, except for the highest plateau and mountain surfaces. Lowland Canada is snow-free right to the Arctic coast of Ellesmere Island in 80°N.

In glacial times, this was not so. We cannot say why the energy was not then sufficient to get rid of each winter's snow. But as the snow accumulated, its highly reflective surface must have sent back unused much of the solar radiation received, thereby compounding the cold. Even now, the main reason that the eastern spring is so late is the high reflectivity of the deep snow cover, which rejects much of the energy needed to get rid of it.

We have a few clues as to the future. At present (the early 1970s), regions of Canada east of about 90°W are passing through a period of cold and snowy winters. It appears that this trend is causally related to the anomalous warmth of the western North Pacific. This in turn has strengthened the so-called long-wave disturbances of the overlying westerly winds, which are sweeping a little farther north than usual in Pacific longitudes, and a little farther south over central and eastern North America. As a result, the southward flow of outbreaks of arctic air over eastern Canada is encouraged. There is evidence that similar small changes in the structure of the westerlies occurred about 8,000 years ago, with a marked warming of climate in the western Arctic and Subarctic. We can expect more of such fluctuations, which alter the details of the climate without altering its nature.

If, however, the climate east of Hudson Bay were to become a little cooler, and the level of the land were to rise by a few hundred meters (it is rising slowly now), such a fluctuation would probably start ice sheets growing again over the plateaus of Labrador–Ungava, where even today certain snowbeds survive most summers.

In short, we do not know whether Canada's present climate will revert to the glacial, stay as it is now, or get warmer. All we can say is that there are grounds for fearing the first. It *could* happen, and evidences of the risk can be seen in each abnormally cold, snowy winter and each cool, cloudy summer.

The harsh climate affects the landscape in another and quite different way. This book is concerned with landscapes that, in spite of the large role played by glacial action, have evolved mainly through river erosion and transportation. Except in small areas of the west, the landscape-forming processes are today those of a basically humid climate; and they have been much the same, glacial episodes apart, for a very long time. A humid climate with cold, snowy winters has a very special river regime, and this is critical to the way in which Canada's landscape evolves.

Humid landscape-forming processes work best under extreme conditions. Rivers in flood have enormously greater erosive and transporting power than they have in their more placid phases. The northwest European settlers who first saw Canada's rivers can have had no inkling of their tumultuous power. They saw the rivers first in late summer and fall, when they resemble the sluggish, pastoral rivers of England, northern France, and the Low Countries—the streams of Constable, Turner, and Peter de Wynt. Canada's streams are made of a different fibre. Each spring, as the snowmelt occurs, they have a spectacular flood—the freshet—when for a few weeks they are enormously powerful, attacking their beds and rolling rocks and deadfalls along their courses, as well as sweeping out the winter ice. Nothing like this occurs in Britain and northern France.

Even in summer, the same proneness to violence exists. Everywhere east of the British Columbia Coast Range there is the risk of heavy thunderstorms, which in a few minutes can flood the smaller streams and move quantities of soil or rock down the slopes attacked. The Maritimes, in particular, are often crossed in late summer and fall by Atlantic hurricanes. This year (1971) Halifax received 11.5 inches of rain in forty-eight hours from one such August visitor. Rainfall of this intensity does more work than decades of light falls.

This mixture of cold-climate processes accounts for much of the detail of Canada's landscapes. The familiar landforms for most Canadians are those of recently glaciated landscapes that are now being worked over by streams perhaps 10,000 years old in their present courses. The spring freshet and the brief summer storms have repeated themselves as many times. But on the time scale of geological history, this is only a brief moment. The fundamental basis of Canada, the bedrock structures beneath the surface, is enormously older. So also are the great mountain systems, the major plateaus, and of course the Canadian Shield, around which the entire continent has gradually evolved to its present shape.

The Shield (which is treated at length in the following pages) is one of the great crustal plates forming the oldest, most rigid, and most permanent elements in the earth's surface. Once again, we find a parallel with Scandinavia; it also is largely made up of a great crustal shield. For Canadians, it means that their territories have at their heart an immense, secure, but intractable mass of ancient rocks that make settlement difficult and unattractive, but that yield a high proportion of the country's mineral wealth.

The monotonous plateau surface of the Shield is familiar to many Canadians. The main railways and roads between Winnipeg and the east thread its surface for 1,000 miles, nearly all of which are either thinly settled or empty of man. The Shield ducks beneath the Great Lakes and the St. Lawrence, and underlies much of the American Midwest; in Michigan, Minnesota, and Wisconsin, and in the Adirondack Mountains of New York State, it surfaces south of the United States border. But for the most part it is Canadian, the adamantine core of the country.

It is the only structural province that is almost completely Canada's. The others run more or less north-south across the international border and are shared with the United States. The Maritimes, Newfoundland, and southeastern Quebec are one with New England and the Appalachians. The St. Lawrence Lowlands are an extension of the Midwest. The Prairies and the American Great Plains are part of the same unit. And the Western Cordillera of British Columbia and Alberta extends north into Alaska and south across the continental United States to Central America. The border is completely irrational in relation to the continental grain. Canada's

functioning unity has been bought by forcing, at enormous cost, lines of communication against a grain hostile to penetration. The country represents a triumph of national endeavour against geographical logic.

The border generally makes much more sense in relation to drainage. In British Columbia, however, this is not so. The Columbia–Kootenay system disregards the border, and Canada has been forced into elaborate treaty arrangements in order that its waters may be used constructively. On the Prairies, by contrast, the main drainage is via the Saskatchewan rivers to Hudson Bay, and the border is not very far from the divide with the Missouri drainage. Small parts of Alberta and Saskatchewan drain via the Missouri River to the Gulf of Mexico; indeed, these regions were once considered Spanish territories. Farther east, however, the Souris and Red rivers, which cross the border, drain to Hudson Bay. Winnipeg, in the direct path of the Red River floods on the flat floor of former Lake Agassiz, has good reason to fear Minnesota's run-off.

The Great Lakes–St. Lawrence system, created by the recent glaciations from river systems once tributary to the Mississippi, lies directly on the international border as far as Lake St. Francis, so that Canada and the United States are compelled to manage these water bodies jointly. The Saint John River in New Brunswick, although less important economically, also has this international aspect. Thus, the great river highways of the east have been committed to joint management by arbitrary acts of political boundary making.

These are not the only problems of political geography confronting Canada. The Arctic Archipelago, a huge area of hills, mountains, and ancient river systems now half-drowned by the sea, is unique among the world's geographical oddities. Most of its channels, through which for centuries mariners have sought (and with great hazard found) the Northwest Passage, are heavily ice-choked even in summer. Yet somehow Canada must maintain an effective presence over channels and islands alike. Since enormous reserves of oil and natural gas are now known to lie on the southwestern fringes of the Archipelago, the effort to maintain this presence is no longer simply a desire to assert sovereignty; rather, a watch must be kept over one of the doorways to a key area on the world's resource map.

If this book has a main purpose, it is to make the well-informed Canadian more conscious of the diversity of landscape underlying over-simplified descriptions of the country, and to show him it is worth more than the casual look he usually gives it. There is today an awakening interest in ecology, in the living plant and animal communities that also inhabit Canada, and in their relations with the rest of nature. The rest of nature includes the landforms described and analyzed in this book. Like the wildlife, the forests, and the prairies, these landforms are part of the natural environment of Canadian society. In the past, they played a dominant role in the history of settlement and national expansion. In the future, their role will be more subtle and more complex, but not less vital. Knowledge of Canada's physical landscapes is more than an intellectual attainment: for Canadians, it is one of the keys to a richer and more appealing future.

1

Geological History

Some of the world's oldest known rock occurs in Manitoba; and in the same province, the rich farms of the Red River Valley are built on rock so young that the lake in which it was deposited was seen by some of the early inhabitants of prehistoric America. The geological history of Canada thus extends over the whole expanse of recorded time, from more than 2,700 million years ago to the present. It is a story that is almost as old as the earth, and possibly nearly as old as the universe itself.

The history of the earth extends over five *eras*, the largest units of geological time. These eras are of unequal length, the first two being nearly four times the length of the other three together; these two are probably better named eons than eras. In order of occurrence they are the Archeozoic (or Archean), the Proterozoic, the Paleozoic, the Mesozoic, and the Cenozoic. The Archeozoic and Proterozoic are often lumped together as the Precambrian, a practice that originated in Great Britain, where the total outcrop of rocks dating from these eras is very small in area. Each era is subdivided into periods, which also are of unequal length. Tables 1-1 and 1-2 on pages 9 and 12 show these periods, with their approximate dates as determined by isotopic analysis. Rocks accumulated during a period constitute a *system*; thus we talk about the Ordovician period and the Ordovician system, as we refer to time and the landscape, respectively. Finally, periods are frequently subdivided into epochs and systems into series. The Cenozoic era, for example, is divided into two periods, the Tertiary and the Quaternary (which includes the present); and the Tertiary is further subdivided into epochs: the Paleocene, the Eocene, the Oligocene, the Miocene, and the Pliocene.

The Archean Era

The oldest rocks of the earth's crust, formed earlier than 2,500 million years ago, are usually classed together as the Archean. Rocks of this age make up a large part of the Canadian Shield and form the nucleus of the North American continent. Other rocks of this age occur in the Maritimes and the Western Cordillera, and underlie the younger sedimentary rocks of the Prairies.

The term *Archean* refers to the most ancient of rocks. We can visualize the world at this time as a grim and hostile place with widespread volcanic activity. The land masses were entirely devoid of life and were drab in colour. In the seas, there may have been a few primitive organisms, but even here they were specks in an empty immensity. Somewhere in this ancient desert there were the seeds of the life we know today.

The absence of life in the oldest rocks has made the ordinary method of dating them by the fossil record impossible, and until recently little was known about this early period. In the last decade or so, age determinations have been possible through the use of the potassium-argon ratios in mica and the rubidium-strontium and lead-uranium methods. The results have often been a startling confirmation of earlier deductions based on lithological resemblances and relations to intrusions and unconformities; but while before only rather small areas in the southern Canadian Shield could be studied with sufficient intensity to place them in the geologic column, it is now possible to date several other parts.

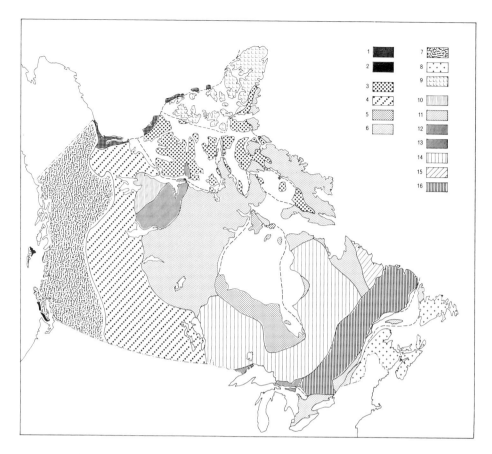

1	7	
2	8	
3	9	
4	10	
5	11	
6	12	
	13	
	14	
	15	
	16	

1	Arctic Coastal Plain		9	Innuitian Orogen
2	Pacific Coastal Plain		10	Bear Province
3	Arctic Platform		11	Churchill Province
4	Interior Platform		12	Slave Province
5	Hudson Platform		13	Southern Province
6	St. Lawrence Platform		14	Superior Province
7	Cordilleran Orogen		15	Nain Province
8	Appalachian Orogen		16	Grenville Province

Fig. 1-1   The geological regions of Canada (after Geological Survey of Canada)

It is evident that the Canadian Shield grew in complexity as a succession of great mountain systems that were comparable to modern mountain belts formed in and around it. The two oldest systems formed the Superior Province, extending from northeastern Manitoba (and under the younger Prairie rocks from western Manitoba) to northern Quebec, and Slave Province northeast of Great Slave Lake. Both areas developed as the result of intense folding towards the end of the Archean era. Fig. 1-2 shows these and other structural provinces of the Shield

The great majority of these rocks—and also of Proterozoic rocks of the succeeding era—are granites and granite gneisses. Indeed, no less than 80 per cent of the entire Shield is made of granite, sometimes little altered and sometimes metamorphosed to gneiss. Granite is, of course, a plutonic rock, and the enormous overlapping batholiths of the Shield must have been consolidated far below the surface of the earth. Here and there in the Shield, we find traces of the pre-existing crustal material enclosed in elongated bodies of metamorphosed sedimentary and volcanic

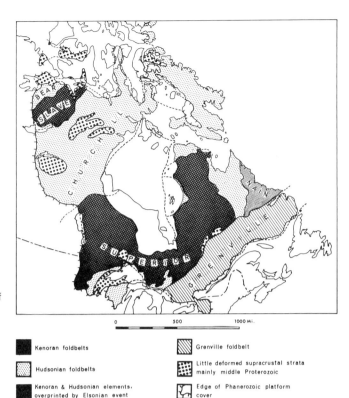

Fig. 1-2   The structural provinces of the Canadian Shield (after Stockwell)

■ Kenoran foldbelts

▨ Grenville foldbelt

Hudsonian foldbelts

▦ Little deformed supracrustal strata mainly middle Proterozoic

Kenoran & Hudsonian elements, overprinted by Elsonian event

Edge of Phanerozoic platform cover

rocks; of these, the sediments must have been derived from the erosion of earlier land masses. The lavas in many cases flowed over the sea floor, and subsequently, the minerals have been changed. They are often known as greenstone, after the colour they developed after metamorphism. The granites of the Shield, although of incredible age, are in no sense the original crust of the earth. It is a fascinating thought that some day, in and among the batholiths, we may hit upon a fragment of the first surface, formed as the earth cooled.

In several of the sedimentary-volcanic Archean areas, a sequence has been recognized of a group of predominantly volcanic rocks separated by an unconformity from sediments that includes a basal conglomerate. The lower unit was given the name Keewatin, after the area where it occurs in northwestern Ontario. The rocks consist of vast sheets of basaltic or andesitic lavas, often displaying the pillow structure that is developed in volcanic rocks cooled in water. There are small patches of sediments, however, in which volcanic ash, sandstones and some clays were deposited, probably in small ponds and lakes. In some places (notably in Minnesota's Vermilion Range), the sediments are rich in iron oxides. The upper unit has been called the Timiskaming. In addition to the basal conglomerate, it includes sandstone, shales, and greywackes. This last rock-type is especially common; since it consists of fragments of only partially decomposed rock, it presumably indicates rapid erosion. Although both these terms, Keewatin and Timiskaming, were once applied widely throughout the Shield, they are now reserved for the type areas which they first described.

The Proterozoic Era

Within the Canadian Shield are many areas of rock which differ strikingly from the Archean rocks already described. These rocks are sedimentary and volcanic in origin; and instead of being included in the granites, they

TABLE 1-1

THE GEOLOGICAL TIME SCALE IN
CANADA: THE MAIN MOUNTAIN-
BUILDING EPISODES

Eon	Era	Age: 10^6 years	Orogeny	Period
Phanerozoic	Cenozoic	65	Laramide	Cretaceous/Tertiary
			Columbian	Jurassic/Cretaceous
	Mesozoic			
		230		
			Appalachian	Carboniferous
	Paleozoic		Acadian	Devonian/Carboniferous
			Taconian	Ordovician/Silurian
		600		
	Hadrynian			
		955		
			Grenvillian	
Proterozoic	Helikian	1370	Elsonian	
		1735		
			Hudsonian	
	Aphebian			
		2480		
			Kenoran	
Archean				

Precambrian time (the Proterozoic and Archean
eras) was four times as long as the Phanerozoic era,
the period of obvious life.

overlie them unconformably. They are referred to the Proterozoic era and consist of sandstone, limestone, dolomite, and lavas that were laid down in the shallower seas at the inner margin of geosynclines and in continental waters. In places, the Proterozoic rocks contain iron formations, and the rich Lake Superior and Labrador Trough ores are of this age.

For long it was thought that the majority of Proterozoic rocks had escaped folding completely, or were only mildly folded. It is now clear, however, that although many of the Proterozoic series are shallow-water sediments lying on a basement of older rocks, in addition long narrow seas existed in which a broad range of shallow and deep-water sediments and volcanic rocks were deposited. This has been shown from the Labrador Trough, where shallow-water sediments on the southwest (landward) side are folded, converted to gneiss, and intruded by granites away from the "continent" on the northeast of the Trough.

The Proterozoic rocks contain a few undoubted calcareous algae and many specks of carbon, probably of organic origin. Forms in the rock resembling worm casts, some sponge spicules, and fossil seaweed are about all that remain of what may have been fairly abundant life at the end of Precambrian time. Elsewhere, the rocks are devoid of fossils. Once again, correlation by the ordinary methods of dating is impossible and the geologist is forced to use isotope measurements.

In the Proterozoic era, there were apparently three major mountain-building periods or orogenies, during which further broad areas of rock were added to or modified from the earlier Archean provinces. These include several small provinces and the large Churchill Province, which extends from northern Saskatchewan to northern Labrador and includes all the northern sector of the Shield.

Probably the best-known Proterozoic rocks in Canada are the Huronian, which cross northern Ontario from Sault Ste. Marie along the north shore of Lake Huron past Sudbury to northwestern Quebec. They consist of quartzites, conglomerates, and mudstones. Within these Huronian rocks is the Gowganda Formation, a hard, massive conglomerate consisting of striated and polished boulders set in a fine-grained, originally clay-rich ground mass. The formation is known as a tillite, and the resemblance to the glacial till spread across the same areas by the recent Laurentide ice sheet (see Chapter 2) is astonishing. A similar formation, the Coleman, found near Cobalt, Ontario, may also be a tillite.

Even more problematical is the age of a broad zone of rocks in the Grenville Province that extends nearly 300 miles from Lake Huron and central Ontario across the Shield in southern Quebec to southern Labrador. These rocks are complex granitized sedimentary gneisses that are associated with crystalline limestones and a little lava. For a long time, geologists thought they were Archean, but recent isotopic age determinations suggest they were folded and metamorphosed about 1,000 million years ago. This would place them in the youngest part of the Proterozoic era, although the original sediments may be much older.

In several parts of the Shield, flat-lying and only slightly altered sediments commonly associated with basaltic lavas cover the basement rocks. Extensive areas of these sedimentary rocks, which are of Proterozoic age, are found west of Hudson Bay, including the Athabasca sandstones south of Lake Athabasca, the Dubawnt sandstone in the Thelon Basin, and the Coppermine series south of Coronation Gulf and in Bathurst Inlet. Similar rocks form the Keweenawan series in the Lake Superior district. Wherever they occur, these rocks produce unusual scenery for the Shield. In central Keewatin and Mackenzie, they form monotonously flat plains occasionally broken by cuestas or flat-topped mesas. Elsewhere the basalt lavas produce magnificent scarplands and steep-sided plateaus, particularly around Coronation Gulf.

With the close of Grenvillian mountain building, crustal activity in the Shield was reduced. Precambrian time was drawing to a conclusion, and life was about to launch upon its great evolutionary process. The Canadian Shield was consolidated; ever since the Grenville disturbance, it has remained essentially a rigid nucleus around which later mountain chains developed. Although seas have spread across the Shield and it is today more than half buried by sediments, they have remained unwarped and in many areas unfaulted.

The Paleozoic Era

The Paleozoic era lasted about 300 million years, and is divided into six or seven periods. During this lapse of time, life blossomed forth in the seas and climbed onto the land.

Plate 1-1   A rafted pebble in Gowganda varved sediments probably associated with a Precambrian glaciation: Espanola, Ontario. (Geological Survey of Canada, Ottawa.)

Even in the oldest Paleozoic rocks (the Cambrian system), there is a rich record of marine animal life, for many of the dominant groups of the modern world had already evolved. It is difficult to understand why there is so little trace in the Proterozoic sediments of the evolutionary ancestors of this rich fauna. A few lowly plants in the Proterozoic era, and then, in the Cambrian period, highly organized and differentiated marine life—the contrast remains a mystery. By the end of Paleozoic times, thick forests cloaked the land masses, upon which a complex animal kingdom was already established. For the first time in our story, accurate dating of the rocks by fossil content becomes possible.

The trilobites, brachiopods, graptolites, and other fossils that make this dating possible also enable us to reconstruct the Paleozoic shorelines with some approach to certainty. This patient research is known as *paleography*. We are very far from understanding the sweeping changes of shoreline that took place in Canada in Paleozoic times, but we are at least able to hazard well-informed guesses once the fossil record appears.

Throughout the era, the heartland around which the continent expanded was the Canadian Shield. From time to time, particularly in the Ordovician period, the sea spread

TABLE 1-2

THE GEOLOGICAL TIMETABLE IN
THE LAST 600,000,000 YEARS

Era	Period	Epoch	Date: beginning of interval (in millions of years)
Cenozoic	Quaternary	Recent	.01
		Pleistocene	2.0
	Tertiary	Pliocene	5.5
		Miocene	22.5
		Oligocene	36
		Eocene	53.5
		Paleocene	65
Mesozoic	Cretaceous		135
	Jurassic		180
	Triassic		230
Paleozoic	Permian		280
	Pennsylvanian	Carboniferous	310
	Mississippian		345
	Devonian		405
	Silurian		425
	Ordovician		510
	Cambrian		600

widely across the Precambrian continent, depositing extensive sheets of sedimentary rock, particularly limestone, upon the ancient basement. Subsequently, when the Shield was above the waves, stream erosion swept away part of this younger cover. Large areas of it remain in the Prairies, however, with smaller patches along the south shore of Hudson Bay, in the southern Arctic islands, in southern Ontario and the St. Lawrence Lowlands. In the central and western Prairies, the Paleozoic rocks in turn were buried by later sediments, but elsewhere they form the surface rocks. Rarely are they folded. It seems that the massive strength of the Shield has never since yielded to compressive forces on a mountain-building scale. Faulting, by contrast, is quite common, and some of the Paleozoic outliers that were once part of the cover rocks on the Shield occur in distinct downfaulted depressions or *graben*. They include the Ordovician limestones in the fault basin of Lake St. John and the lowland at the head of Frobisher Bay on Baffin Island.

On the margins of the Shield, the story was very different. In these areas, there were three great geosynclines, elongated seas, in which vast quantities of debris were deposited from adjacent continental land masses. The eastern trough was the *Appalachian–Acadian geosyncline*, corresponding closely in position to the present-day mountain system of the same name. The Canadian Shield to the northwest had been reduced to a peneplain before Paleozoic times, and the streams flowing off it were presumably lightly laden for much of the era. On the southeastern flank, however, there seems to have been a continental land mass of considerable size and relief; great quantities of sand, clay, and muds were deposited in the geosyncline from this shore. In Devonian times, for example, a large river discharging somewhere south of the modern site of Albany built up the great pile of deltaic sediments that now form the magnificent east-facing cuesta of the Catskill Mountains in New York State. Acadia, as the supposed continent is called, remains an enigma whose present status is confused; probably, it was identical with western Europe before the two continents split apart with continental drift.

The western trough is known as the *Cordilleran geosyncline*. A large trough of deposition lay along the north-south axis of the

Plate 1-2   Late Paleozoic sediments, laid down horizontally; earth movements have tilted vertically the sandstone ripples and the shale mud cracks: Parrsboro, N.S.

present-day Western Cordillera as early as Proterozoic times: the Beltian group of sedimentary rocks that forms the impressive Front Range of the Rockies in Waterton Lakes (Alberta) and Glacier (Montana) national parks accumulated within it. This ancient geosyncline apparently persisted throughout Paleozoic times in western Canada, although at times the sea withdrew from part of its huge extent. The Canadian Shield along its eastern flank (now beneath the Prairies) was presumably of low relief throughout the era; and to explain the great thicknesses of sediment that accumulated in the trough, geologists have postulated a vast and rugged land mass lying to the west. *Cascadia*—like Acadia, of which it is the western equivalent—is a geological mystery, and there are many who question whether it ever had the status of a subcontinent.

The northern trough was part of the Innuitian region that includes all of Arctic Canada north of Parry Channel except for Shield

areas close to Baffin Bay. The *Franklinian geosyncline*, as the Paleozoic zone of deposition is known, was an L-shaped trough that extended eastwards through the Parry Islands and northeastwards into Ellesmere Island.

Profound unrest within the crust occurred several times during the Paleozoic era in North America and other continents. These disturbances occurred chiefly in and near the great geosynclines of the times. Such troughs of accumulation receive enormous thicknesses of sediments during the long periods of their existence, and yet remain seas, though they are often shallow. Plainly, the floor of the trough must sink to allow this condition to be preserved. The geosyncline therefore becomes a progressively deeper sag in the crust with an ever-increasing load of recent sediments. Ultimately, there comes a point when the stresses can no longer be contained, and faulting is followed by vulcanism, leading to the growth of volcanic island arcs like those that exist today off the east coast of Asia.

Subsequently, compression crushes the contained sediments into complex folds, usually intruded by large granite batholiths. As the *orogeny*, as it is called, comes to an end, general uplift occurs; and the elongated mass of folded sediments, volcanic rocks, and intruded granites rise to form a great mountain system. All the great mountain systems of geological history seem to have originated this way, either on the margins of continents or between continents.

Structural geologists differ on the details of this process, which is far from understood. We need not concern ourselves with the mechanisms, however, for the evidence is plain for all to read: the great mountain systems of Canada, past and present, are all made up of belts of folded, contorted sedimentary and volcanic rocks, often metamorphosed by pressure and heat to a point where recognition becomes difficult.

The three great Paleozoic geosynclines differed in stability. In that of the west, the Cordilleran, deposition continued in Paleozoic times, if not without break, at least without major crises. Vulcanism occurred from time to time, and lava beds exist within the sedimentary pile. On the whole, however, the Paleozoic era was a period of calm with only local orogenic activity. It presents a striking contrast to the catastrophes of ensuing Mesozoic times.

Along the northern edge of the continent, the Franklinian geosyncline experienced major folding in the Ellesmerian Orogeny of late Devonian to early Pennsylvanian age, which resulted in the Parry Island, Central Ellesmere, and Northern Ellesmere fold belts (Fig. 1-3). As the Franklinian geosyncline came to an end, a second area of deposition developed to the northwest in the Sverdrup Basin; and it continued to accumulate sediments from the Pennsylvanian to the Upper Cretaceous period. The basin then underwent the Eurekan Orogeny.

The Atlantic Provinces and Eastern Quebec

In the east, mountain building was complex; the Appalachian–Acadian geosyncline was overwhelmed by three major disturbances, which together created the Eastern Cordillera of modern North America. The first of these was the *Taconic Orogeny*, which came in late Ordovician times. This led to intense folding, with a large-scale northwestward thrusting that carried the folded, often fine-grained

Plate 1-3   A gypsum dome injected through the surrounding rocks during a recent phase of Innuitian mountain building: Queen Elizabeth Islands.

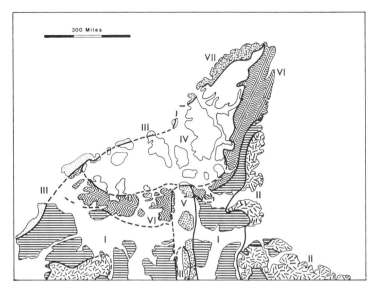

Fig. 1-3   The structure of the Queen Elizabeth Islands

Folded zones:
I   Sverdrup Basin
II Northern Ellesmere
III Parry Islands and
    Central Ellesmere
IV Boothia Arch
Stable zones:
V   Platform sedimentaries
VI Canadian Shield
VII Coastal Plain

sediments of the central depositional zone (usually known as the eugeosyncline) as much as 30 miles across the undisturbed shallow-water, marginal-shelf (known as miogeosyncline) beds of similar age in what are now the St. Lawrence and Champlain valleys. The Champlain (or Logan) thrust-fault marks the outer limit of this folding.

The disturbance was accompanied by vulcanism. In the Eastern Townships of Quebec, basic intrusions of this period have subsequently been altered to serpentine, from which large quantities of asbestos are now produced. By the time the Taconic Revolution was concluded, a great mountain range comparable to the present-day Rockies extended from the Atlantic Provinces to the southeastern United States.

Throughout the Silurian and early Devonian periods, the Taconic Mountains were denuded and sediments were again accumulating. Deposition came to an end with the commencement of the *Acadian Orogeny*. During this disturbance, the deepest part of the geosyncline melted and granites were formed; today they underlie the rugged hills of the Central Highlands of New Brunswick, the Atlantic Uplands, and broad areas of southern Newfoundland.

The Acadian Mountains produced in the second orogeny were in turn eroded. The third orogenic cycle that followed did not repeat in eastern Canada the previous cycles, as activity in the Appalachian Revolution (as it is called) was centred in the southern Appalachians and deformation was not severe in the north.

Sedimentation began in early Carboniferous (Mississippian) times in isolated fault basins, the deposits including non-marine sandstones and shales, salt, anhydrite, and gypsum. In late Carboniferous (Pennsylvanian) times, the sea withdrew from the geosyncline and it became a vast, swampy plain on which grew luxuriant forests. The largest lowland extended over the central United States, while smaller plains existed in the Maritimes. Tree-ferns, horse-tails, and other primitive trees formed the forest. They spread layer after layer of vegetable litter on the ground. Although periodically overwhelmed by invasions of the sea or by the flood-plain deposits of the ancient Mississippi, these forests reasserted themselves for millions of years. And so, layer by layer, the coal deposits of the east were built up. The thickness and continuity of these layers was greatest in the east-central United States, where the

Pennsylvania and West Virginia basins today make up the world's largest coal field. In what is now Canada, the deposits were thinner and less continuous, and coal seams were relatively few; moreover, they have since suffered grievously from erosion. Even so, considerable deposits remain in Cape Breton Island and the lowlands of eastern New Brunswick and northern Nova Scotia.

Very similar conditions were experienced at the same time in Eurasia. It is a major geological mystery how the very special conditions required for the deposition of coal measures could have been maintained over so great a period of time, and over so huge an extent of space. The genial, humid climate needed for the forest growth is also noteworthy.

By the end of the Carboniferous epoch, the Paleozoic orogenies in eastern North America were almost finished. Some activity continued into the Mesozoic era; and during the Triassic period in the Maritimes, fault basins were formed that were filled with

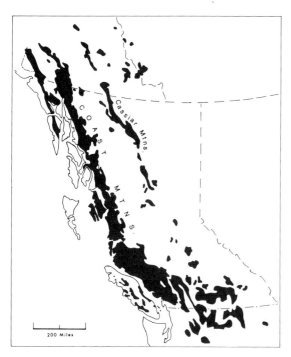

Fig. 1-4   Granite intrusions in western Canada during the Columbian mountain-building episode

bright red muds, sands, and pebble beds. Associated with the faulting was volcanic activity, and basalt lavas poured over the land burying the clastic rocks. Today the basalt cap rock that forms North Mountain in Nova Scotia is a visible reminder of this period.

By this time, the main structural elements of eastern Canada were largely consolidated; the Canadian Shield, the St. Lawrence and Ontario lowlands, and the Appalachian–Acadian Province were already distinct. From that day forward, only limited invasions of the sea and minor changes of structure have been experienced. Our story in the next era shifts to other parts of Canada.

The Mesozoic Era

We have reached a point in time a little more than 200 million years ago; more than 90 per cent of the provable life of the earth has already passed, yet we are still immeasurably distant from the familiar world of modern man. Mesozoic time, some 150 million years of earth history, marks the span extending from the formation of the Appalachians to the creation of the Rockies at the close of the Cretaceous period. It was the era of the great reptiles, who dominated land, sea, and air, and gave to the world's fauna a bizarre quality best expressed by the dragons of children's fables. It was also the time during which the land plants evolved towards the dominant forms we know today, although our knowledge of the stages by which this came about is pitifully meagre.

In the west, however, the Mesozoic was an era of ceaseless and dramatic change; sedimentation continued throughout the era, although with interruptions both in what are now the Prairie Provinces and in the Cordilleran geosyncline to the west. In the latter, in Triassic times the deposits were thick limestones, shales, and volcanic beds; but through the Jurassic and early Cretaceous periods, there seems to have been a halting progression towards shallow-water and terrestrial deposits. At the beginning of the late Cretaceous, the last of the great continental transgressions occurred, and sediments were laid down in a sea that at first covered all the Prairies and western Mackenzie. As the period progressed, the sea withdrew intermittently, and brackish water and terrestrial conditions prevailed. Reptiles ranged over the Prairies and their bones were incorporated into the rocks as they were formed, particularly in Alberta. The shales, clays, and sandstone of this period are nearly 2,000 feet thick in western Manitoba and about 5,500 feet in southern Alberta. Underlying the glacial sediments, they are the dominant surface rocks of the Prairies.

During part of the Cretaceous period, conditions over much of the west favoured the development of luxuriant forests, akin to the forests of the east in later Carboniferous times. Coal seams of vast extent underlie the Prairies today, and occur in folded and isolated basins from the Rockies to the Pacific.

Western Cordillera

At no time during the Mesozoic era did the western geosyncline stay quiet for long. Volcanic rocks at various levels of the succession show that, as in recent geological history, crustal instability was the general rule. In middle Jurassic times began the *Columbian disturbance*, which folded and metamorphosed the rocks of the country now along the Pacific; such batholiths constitute the core of the peninsula of Lower California (Mexico) and the Sierra Nevada. The largest underlies the Coast Range of British Columbia, and stretches for nearly 1,300 miles from northern Washington State through the length of British Columbia into Yukon Territory; it varies in width from 30 to over 120 miles. The focus of the orogeny shifted eastwards until the close of Cretaceous time, when the disturbance merged with a larger one known as the Laramide Orogeny, which affected the eastern part of the Cordilleran geosyncline. The mass of rocks, folded and intensely faulted, today forms the Rocky Mountains and adjacent ranges, and has visibly been thrust eastwards over the less

disturbed rocks of the foothills, probably for many tens of miles.

Although the Laramide Revolution began in the Cretaceous period, movements continued until the Oligocene epoch; indeed, throughout the Cenozoic and right to the present day, local deposition, faulting, and vulcanism have occurred. The enormous basalt-flows of the Columbia Plateau in Washington, Oregon, and Idaho were formed, presumably by fissure eruption, in Miocene and Pliocene times. Finally, in the Pliocene epoch, there was a renewed convulsion along the Pacific coast, sometimes known as the *Cascadian disturbance*, which led to large uplifts, faulting, and some folding of the most recent sediments and volcanics. Thus it can be seen that the structural history of the Western Cordillera is extremely long and complex; there were at least three major phases of mountain building—Columbian, Laramide, and Cascadian—extending over more than 100 million years.

The Cenozoic Era

The Cenozoic era is divided by geologists into two periods, the Tertiary and the Quaternary (which includes the present time). Since Quaternary time seems to have lasted no more than two million years, the Tertiary period represents about sixty-three million, comparing in length with the periods of the Paleozoic era. Sedimentation and mountain building continued in parts of Canada throughout the Cenozoic. It is also the era when the landscape developed the features we recognize today. Towards the end it was marked by two exceptional events: the Ice Ages and the appearance of man.

We have seen that in the northern islands the Franklinian geosyncline was succeeded by the Sverdrup Basin, in which deltaic, marine, and volcanic products were deposited throughout the Mesozoic era and into the early Tertiary period. As the sedimentation phase ended, there was widespread folding associated with the injection of gypsum and anhydrite from the bottom of the basin.

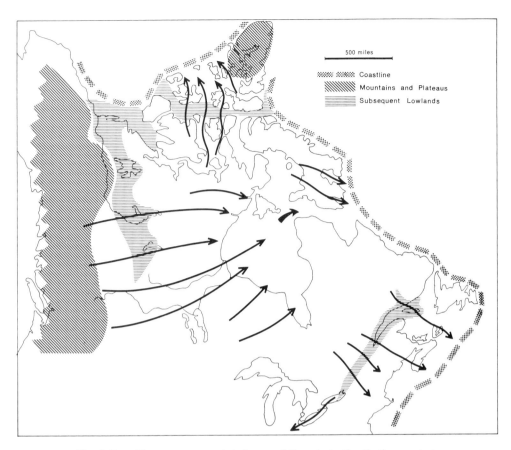

Fig. 1-5   The reconstructed drainage of Canada in the Tertiary period

These rocks broke through the younger rocks and reached the surface as domes along the axis of the deepest part of the basin from Ellef Ringnes to Axel Heiberg Island. These events did not terminate Cenozoic deposition in the Arctic; they were followed by the spread of sands and gravels, the Beaufort Formation, over the western Arctic islands.

It was noted in the previous section that widespread crustal activity continued in the Western Cordillera from the Cretaceous into the Tertiary period. The mountains that were formed at this time were attacked by erosion in the Tertiary period; and the muds, sands, gravels, and pebbles that resulted were deposited over much of the Prairies, just as they were in the Cretaceous period. The environment was at first marine; but it quickly became terrestrial, and fluvial beds were spread out as vast alluvial fans, comprised mainly of

coarse material. The deposits are found as far east as Turtle Mountain and here, as in many other parts, contain lignite seams. The Tertiary rocks have been strongly denuded in the recent past, but in general they are thickest close to the Alberta foothills.

The Face of Canada in the Tertiary Period

Mountain building and the deposition of sediments were not the only events of importance to affect Canada in the Tertiary period. Almost all the eastern part of the country was dry land, and on it the forces of erosion were carving out a landscape in which many of the major elements of the present scenery were recognizable. By the end of the Tertiary period, this was also true of western Canada.

The Rockies had been uplifted already in

18   *The Natural Landscapes of Canada*

Cretaceous times, but they were reduced to a range of low relief before they were again elevated and deeply dissected by rivers and ice to form the existing magnificent scenery.

We described earlier how the sediments from the Rockies were carried east by rivers, forming the present Tertiary surface rocks of part of the Prairies. Many of these rivers probably flowed right across the Prairies and the Canadian Shield, eventually converging as one major river in the Hudson Bay Basin (Fig. 1-5). The Saskatchewan rivers and their extension, the Nelson, maintain this course to the present. How many other rivers followed a parallel course is not known, but they may have extended from a Liard–Thelon River in the Northwest Territories at least as far south as the United States border.

Although the Tertiary rivers in the western part of the plains had roughly the same elevation as they have today, conditions farther east were very different. The Shield west of Hudson Bay was still partly covered with the limestone that had been deposited during the great Ordovician transgression. Slowly the rivers cut down to the Shield rocks beneath, thus producing many of the contemporary discordancies between the geological structure and the drainage pattern west of Hudson Bay.

These major consequent rivers were not allowed to continue flowing to the northeast indefinitely because two rivers, the early Mississippi–Missouri and the Mackenzie, were extending their courses by headward erosion in the deep, unfolded, and often easily eroded beds that lay between the foothills of the Western Cordillera and the more resistant rocks of the Canadian Shield and the Appalachian Province. With the growth of north-south rivers, capture was inevitable and progressively the Mackenzie added to its drainage basin the Liard, Hay, Peace, and Athabasca rivers. Indeed, it seems that it will be only a matter of time—although in a geological sense—before the last of the old consequents, the North Saskatchewan, follows the fate of the other rivers and is diverted to the Mackenzie.

Hudson Bay at this time was almost certainly a subaerial basin. This great depression in the crust was already in existence in the Paleozoic era; and although it was filled with sediments at that time, it remained a collecting basin for the Tertiary rivers from the west. From an early period, they drained to the Atlantic through Hudson Strait, which has an obscure—though undoubtedly ancient—history. The Hudson Bay Basin may have continued to be land until well into the Pleistocene epoch, for the remnants of a subaerial valley pattern may be traced on the floor of the bay.

On the north side of the Hudson drainage was a different system created by roughly parallel rivers flowing to the north. The division between the two changed, but at one period it lay along the Arctic mainland. These northern rivers drained into Sverdrup Basin; and, as the rocks in it were folded, they appear to have extended across the basin to the Arctic Ocean. The Archipelago was at that time dry land, and sea level was several hundred feet lower than it is today. The rivers became entrenched between plateaus and—like the old consequent rivers in western Canada—were eventually truncated by the growth of secondary rivers, from the Arctic Ocean in the west and from Davis Strait in the east, which cut back along a major zone of crustal weakness that is today Parry Channel. The sea level eventually rose and the former valleys were submerged, dividing the District of Franklin into a complex archipelago.

At the time, a third major drainage system had its source in a height of land in the southeast of the Canadian Shield, roughly along a line from the Lake Abitibi region to central Labrador. From it, rivers flowed south and southeastwards across what are today the St. Lawrence Lowlands and the Gulf of St. Lawrence, through New England and the Maritimes to the Atlantic. The identity of these rivers is speculative; but they may include the south-flowing streams of the Canadian Shield, such as the Coulonge, North River, St. Maurice, and in New England the Connecticut and Kennebec rivers. In New Brunswick, a former river that can be traced through wind gaps, from the upper Saint John and then across the central plain of New Brunswick, was part of the same group; so, too, was a river flowing past Anticosti Island and through Cabot Strait to the Atlantic, the shores of which lay on the outer edge of the continental shelf.

While the pattern of the Canadian drainage is uncertain, two facts stand out clearly. First, for a time at least, the sea level was lower than it is today; and in late Tertiary or possibly early Pleistocene times, rivers were flowing across the continental shelf and particularly the Gulf of St. Lawrence. Just how much lower the sea was relative to the land, and indeed if it was the same amount everywhere, is unknown; but it was clearly several hundreds of feet lower. Equally important, this happened *before* the Ice Ages. This early phase therefore must not be confused with low sea-level stages which occurred during glaciation and which were world-wide in distribution (see Chapter 5).

The other obvious feature is that younger rivers have broken up the initial pattern, so that it is barely visible in the scenery today. These later or subsequent rivers developed on the weaker, generally unfolded sedimentary rocks, particularly those rocks that lay between the Canadian Shield and the Appalachian–Acadian region. These are the rocks of the St. Lawrence Lowlands; and by the end of Tertiary times, two or perhaps three rivers—the predecessors of the St. Lawrence —drained it. The one about which we are most certain flowed from the Saguenay along the St. Lawrence estuary to join the river already mentioned in the Gulf and Cabot Strait. Farther west, there are several possibilities; one of the most likely is that the Ottawa flowed through the Lake Champlain gap between the Adirondacks and the Green Mountains. This river was fed by smaller tributaries from the vicinity of Quebec City. Another river probably flowed from the eastern Ontario basin past Dundas, Ontario, to Lake Erie and so to the Mississippi. Although evidence for this pattern in the east is at best fragmentary, the hypothesis describes the drainage patterns on the floor of the Gulf of St. Lawrence and the wind gaps in the Notre Dame Mountains and Gaspé. The immaturity of the present St. Lawrence—particularly above Montreal, where it may not be older than the last interglacial—resulted from the capture of the middle and western subsequent rivers by the (lower) St. Lawrence as it extended headwards.

This account has emphasized the erosive action of the rivers in shaping the landscape in Tertiary times, but there is no reason to suppose that the crust remained absolutely stable. Throughout much of eastern Canada, there are broad flat rock plains, often incorrectly called peneplains, which were denuded by rivers and which are now several hundreds of feet, and in the Canadian Shield 2,000–6,000 feet, above sea level. One way to explain these features is to think of the continent as a solid, stable block into whose sides the rivers cut a series of horizontal steps. Such stability for tens of millions of years seems improbable when one considers the catastrophic changes that were occurring elsewhere in the world during the Tertiary period. It is more likely that some of the upland surfaces, particularly rather narrow ones close to sea level such as those in New Brunswick and Prince Edward Island, are a result of fairly recent changes in the level of the sea; and the very high surfaces, particularly levels that occur in the Torngat Mountains of Labrador and in the Penny Highlands of eastern Baffin Island (at over 6,000 feet), may be associated with Tertiary crustal movements.

If these events are obscure, it is evident that, by the end of the Tertiary period, Canada in broad outline was very much as we know it today. Certainly, the main elements of the landscape, the great mountains and the broad lowlands, were already in being. The minor changes, the details of the picture, were to come in the ensuing period, the Quaternary. In later Tertiary times, there were signs that a great crisis in world climate was approaching. The northern lands were growing colder, and luxuriant forests that once covered even the Arctic lands began to retreat towards the tropics. In the seas, there was a progressive increase in cold-water forms of life and low-temperature chemical reactions. The world seemed to be taking on a harsh aspect. The Ice Ages were about to start.

Selected Readings

Clark, T. H., and C. W. Stearn, *Geological Evolution of North America*, New York, The Ronald Press, 1968, 570 pp.

Douglas, R. J. W. (ed.), *Geology and Economic Minerals of Canada*, Ottawa, Queen's Printer, 1971, 838 pp.

Dunbar, C. O., and K. M. Waage, *Historical Geology*, New York, Wiley, 1969, 556 pp.

Eicher, D. L., *Geologic Time*, Englewood Cliffs, N.J., Prentice-Hall, 1968, 149 pp.

Gass, I. G., P. J. Smith, and R. C. L. Wilson (eds.), *Understanding the Earth*, Sussex, The Artemis Press, 1971, 355 pp.

Jacobs, J. A., R. D. Russell, and J. T. Wilson, *Physics and Geology*, New York, McGraw-Hill, 1959, 424 pp.

Longwell, C. R., R. F. Flint, and J. E. Sanders, *Physical Geology*, New York, Wiley, 1969, 685 pp.

2

The Great Ice Age

The extraordinary story of the final million years of earth-history is now before us. In the pages that follow, we shall tell of the repeated overwhelming of Canada by vast masses of glacial ice. During these remarkable years, life itself was driven from the country, lingering perhaps in only the remotest valleys of the Yukon, then returning as the ice sheets melted. The last retreat ended only 6,000 years ago; at that time, the ice was banished to the mountains, to Greenland, and to parts of the Arctic islands. The forests and prairies are back, although Canada's cold winters are annual reminders that the recovery is still incomplete. Everything conspires, in fact, to convince us that the relief is only temporary, and that the glaciers will once again expand and reoccupy the country, though not in the immediate future!

These theories about the recent geological past have been held for barely a century. Although the mid-twentieth century accepts the Great Ice Age as a proven fact, in the early 1900s there were still some who rejected it. In Canada, some of the most important research on the glacial deposits was carried out by men who were sure that they were examining the traces of floating sea-ice and icebergs, for many found it impossible to believe that Canada and northern Europe might recently have been what Greenland is today—a vast, silent immensity of inland ice.

The idea of an Ice Age was born in Europe, where there are scattered deposits of far-travelled, grooved, and striated boulders (these are called erratics, because they are far from their original home). Boulders from the Alps litter the Bavarian and Swiss plateaus, and can be picked up on the slopes of the Jura. Stones of unmistakably Scandinavian origin are common in eastern England, northern Germany, and Poland. At first, the wandering field naturalists were inclined to think that these erratics were evidence of a great flood, perhaps of the Biblical flood itself. The great size of some of the erratics and the curious, structureless appearance of the sands and clays in which they occurred (the *drift* of British quarrymen and geologists) bothered the proponents of this view, for the deposits were unlike true water-laid beds.

We may never know precisely who first suggested that the drift and the erratics were glacier-borne. That great but unreadable Scottish pioneer James Hutton is said to have been a convinced glacialist. In any case, the peasant folk of mountain valleys must surely have been aware for centuries of the advance and retreat of glaciers in the Alps and in Norway. Early in the nineteenth century, a number of naturalists and geologists (as yet a scanty breed), sensing the truth of this belief of the mountain folk, suggested that the alpine glaciers had formerly expanded greatly beyond the foot of the mountains, leaving a trail of erratics behind them; and it was not long before the logical, though breath-taking, step was made to the idea that greater glaciers had spread out from the polar regions during a recent cold epoch of geological history.

But the real proponent of the Great Ice Age was a Swiss zoologist named Louis Agassiz. He justified and popularized the idea of glaciation among European scientists, and he was above all the man who first really grasped the immensity of the Ice Age, and of the sweeping changes in world climate that it entailed. In modern Canada, the city of Winnipeg is built on the clays deposited on the floor of a great but vanished lake, whose northern shore was the receding front of the last glacier. This enormous extinct water-body (of which lakes Winnipeg, Winnipegosis, and Manitoba are shrunken remnants) is called Lake Agassiz in the memory of this remarkable Swiss pioneer.

In North America, the new ideas caught men's minds very early. In 1846, Agassiz came to Harvard. His advocacy stimulated tremendous interest, but made few converts for two decades. Today the debate is over. We know as surely as we know anything about the earth's past that repeated cold periods have buried the northern continents in ice during the last million years. We have reconstructed the ancient outlines of each glacier, and can tell approximately the story of its waxing and waning. To Canadians, this story is vital, for almost every part of the country bears the imprint of glacier ice.

Before we go on to the detailed evidence, however, let us think for a moment about the *Pleistocene* epoch, as this period of Cenozoic time is called. Careful analyses of the depths of decay of glacial deposits in the American Midwest have suggested that Pleistocene time began about a million years ago. This figure has been widely accepted, both in North America and in Europe. The method used is subject to one drastic defect: the age of the youngest deposits has to be assumed, and all older dates are in effect calculated as multiples of this assumed age. The figure of a million years just quoted is based on an age of 25,000 years for the latest drift. Recently, however, dating of these deposits with the help of radiocarbon has revised their presumed age to less than half this figure, and this shrinks the Pleistocene epoch to less than 500,000 years. But recent dates of deep-sea deposits formed as the oceans were cooling at the beginning of Pleistocene time suggest this occurred two million years ago!

There is thus considerable uncertainty about the length of the Pleistocene stage—more, indeed, than about many of the vastly older geological epochs. One thing appears clear, however: man, a tool-making primate, first appeared on the earth early in the period, for we find his crude stone implements (and, very rarely, parts of his skeleton) in deposits that can be proved to be of Pleistocene date. Yet, strangely enough, he seems to have shunned the New World. Not until the time of the last glaciation—perhaps the last 40,000 years—can we prove his presence in North America. It may be that he is truly a recent arrival; or it may equally be that we have not yet looked hard enough for his earlier remains.

During the fluctuating climate of Pleistocene times, primitive man seems to have advanced his cultural attainments with staggering slowness. We refer to this Old Stone Age in the history of man as the Paleolithic age. The extraordinary explosion of man's technical genius, which brought him through the Neolithic to the ages of metals and ultimately to his modern mastery, all this has been the work of the past 9,000 years. It did not begin, in fact, until the last relics of the glaciers were beginning their final decline.

The Evidence from Existing Glaciers

A glacier is a mass of ice formed by the slow accumulation and compression of snow. In regions where the annual snowfall exceeds the combined losses by melting, evaporation, and sublimation (evaporation of solid snow or ice), a glacier must form, and will grow until its annual wastage (called *ablation*) just balances the accumulation of snowfall on its surface. With its birth a section of the earth's crust vanishes from the sight, to be subjected to a long agony of compression and abrasion.

We will first consider the *alpine* or *valley glaciers*. These are huge rivers of ice that flow imperceptibly along the valleys of high mountains, terminating today within these valleys, but in glacial periods often extending onto the surrounding plains. Such glaciers may discharge from *ice fields* on the high, flat summits of the range, or they may emerge from great rock-amphitheatres (called *cirques*) at the head of the valleys. In either case, they spring from the accumulation of heavy snow

Plate 2-1   Outlet glaciers descending into an ice-filled fiord from an icecap that almost buries the underlying mountains: northeast Baffin Island. Compare with Plate 3-2, which shows an area of similar topography with less ice. (National Air Photo Library, Surveys and Mapping Branch, Department of Energy, Mines and Resources. Photo T241 L-167.)

on the summits. Cirque and valley glaciers perform a notable work of sculpture upon the surrounding mountains; the characteristic landforms of the Rocky Mountain skyline and the Alps in Europe are mainly the products of glacial erosion.

Vastly more disturbing in scale is the second type, the *continental glacier* or ice sheet. Such glaciers are sprawling, dome-shaped masses of ice that entirely blanket the rock beneath. In the past, they have attained diameters of some thousands of miles. Interior Greenland is utterly obliterated by one such ice sheet; Antarctica is almost submerged by another. The glaciers that deployed upon northern Eurasia and America in the glacial episodes of the Pleistocene epoch were ice sheets of this type, though greater in scale. The ice in such glaciers moves slowly outwards under its own weight; this radial motion is very different from the movement of alpine glaciers, which are able to flow (with minor exceptions) only along pre-existing mountain valleys, cut by ordinary stream erosion.

Canada has many alpine glaciers. By far

the finest are those that engulf the St. Elias Mountains of the Yukon. Originating in very large ice fields on the larger summit plateaus, these glaciers descend in slow-moving, frigid magnificence onto the Pacific coast of Alaska, where several combine to form a vast piedmont ice mass called the Malaspina Glacier. Other ice fields and valley glaciers occur within the Coast Range of British Columbia, especially behind Juneau, Alaska (the Juneau ice field is one of the best-studied North American glaciers) and around the flanks of Mount Waddington. This succession of ice cascades is fed by the heavy snowfall dropped by Pacific storms onto the western slopes of the ranges. The eastern slopes, being sheltered from these storms, have much less snow and far fewer glaciers.

The inland ranges of western Canada are drier, especially in the Yukon, and have few large glaciers. The Rockies south of the Peace River are more fortunate, however, and so is the Selkirk Range in British Columbia. Much the best known are the Columbia Ice Field and the spectacular cirque-and-valley glaciers of the Mount Robson massif. The

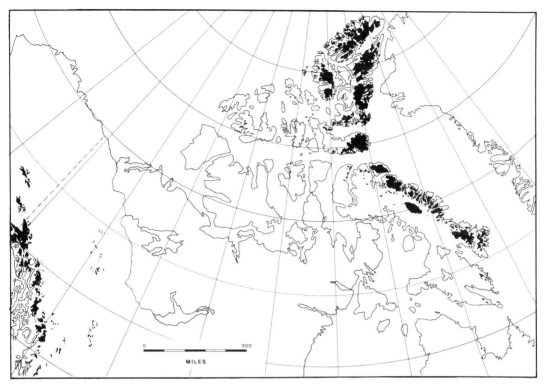

Fig. 2-1   The glaciers of northern Canada

tourist can easily visit most of the Rocky Mountain glaciers.

The mainland of eastern Canada has few true glaciers today. In the Torngat Mountains of northern Labrador, there are several small masses of glacial ice in the bottoms of large cirques that obviously housed larger glaciers in recent times. These tiny *glacierettes*, as they have been called, the largest of which is only a mile long, appear to be on the point of extinction. We have no means of telling whether they are the last relics of the final Pleistocene glacier of North America. Possibly they reformed in the cold, snowy centuries that drove the Norse culture from Greenland.

There are many fine ice fields and alpine glaciers on the eastern Arctic islands (Fig. 2-1). Some of the largest lie on rolling uplands—for example, the Grinnell and Terra Nivea glaciers on the south side of Frobisher Bay. Rather larger is the Barnes Icecap in north-central Baffin Island; this is a low dome

of ice nearly 2,000 feet thick and 85 miles long by 35 miles wide. It is wholly below the altitude at which glacier ice would form under the present climatic conditions, and it may well be a relic of the Pleistocene ice sheet.

Other ice sheets have accumulated on mountain ranges until the ice is so thick that only the highest peaks stick through as *nunataks* (*nunatak* is the Eskimo term for a rocky hill surrounded by glacial ice). Four separate masses of highland ice on Ellesmere Island, others on Axel Heiberg and Bylot Islands, and the Penny Icecap of Baffin Island are all of this type. From them, large tributary glaciers flow down valleys towards the sea. Few of these glaciers reach the sea today, and the icebergs they produce when the ice breaks off are small as compared with icebergs originating in Greenland.

The plateau and highland icecaps comprise the majority of glacier ice in northern Canada. In addition, there are vast numbers of smaller icecaps and cirque-and-valley glaciers along the northeastern edge of the continent. At first sight, it seems remarkable that there is virtually no ice in the central and western Arctic, the only exceptions being some recently discovered ice fields on Melville Island and the dome-shaped icecap that rests on Meighen Island. This last-named ice is unusual in that its oval shape is quite symmetrical; nowhere does it rise above 650 feet. The distribution of the Arctic glaciers must be explained by the restriction of high land to the eastern part of the Innuitian and Shield regions, and by the greater storminess and consequently heavier snowfall as Baffin Bay and the Atlantic Ocean are approached.

One other aspect of the Canadian Arctic glaciers is worth comment. The ice in them is unusually cold. In the low temperatures that prevail throughout the long winters, the temperature in the ice falls far below 0°C; and during the short summers, the amount of sun and water from the melting surface snow are insufficient to raise the temperature to the pressure melting point. The result is that melt water usually fails to sink into the glacier, but instead flows in deep channels on the surface of the ice or in moats between the valley wall and the glacier. In the far north, the sides and front of a glacier are often almost vertical ice walls, and it is impossible to get onto the glacier without special equipment.

Although in Canada there are examples of both major classes of glacier, we must go to Greenland if we want to see a really extensive ice sheet in action. At the glaciers, we can actually watch the processes of glacial erosion and deposition at work. We may talk about the moraines that are visible in southern Ontario, but we can actually go to the Angel Glacier on the side of Mount Edith Cavell in Alberta and see moraines in the making. We may deduce the existence of vast lakes dammed against vanished ice sheets, but we can go to Baffin Island or Ellesmere Island and observe present-day ice-margin lakes. This process of comparison between the mar-

Plate 2-2   Canada's most northerly islands are partly buried beneath ice: the Thompson and White glaciers on Axel Heiberg Island.

TABLE 2-1

SUBDIVISIONS OF THE
PLEISTOCENE EPOCH

North America (Great Lakes)	Northern Europe	Alps	Character
WISCONSIN	WEISCHEL	WURM	Glacial
Sangamon	Eemian		Interglacial
ILLINOIAN	SAALE	RISS	Glacial
Yarmouth	Holstein		Interglacial
KANSAN	ELSTER	MINDEL	Glacial
Aftonian	Cromerian		Interglacial
NEBRASKAN	?	GUNZ	Glacial

ginal areas of existing glaciers and the areas from which the ice has long vanished provides us with evidence to reconstruct the glaciers of the past.

The Story Itself

The story of the glaciation is to be found in the sediments left by the ice and in the unique landforms, both erosional and depositional, that it produced. Additional evidence is obtained from a general knowledge of the climate of icecaps, and from studies of changing sea level and deep-sea deposits, which make it possible to estimate the climate of the Pleistocene epoch.

When the evidence is put together, it seems that almost all of Canada and a large part of the northern United States were buried under vast continental ice sheets on at least four occasions during Pleistocene time. At the climax of each glaciation, Canada disappeared from view except for some mountain peaks; a small area in the Yukon; and, in some glaciations, part of the Baffin Island coast, southern Alberta, and southwestern Saskatchewan. Otherwise the landscape vanished beneath the ice as it expanded to Long Island, to the Ohio Valley, and to the line of the Missouri. Beyond the limits of the ice, the climate was cool; the Deep South was uncomfortably cold in winter, and even the summer was by no means hot.

In spite of its extent, each glaciation came abruptly to a close. The ice sheets melted, shrank, and vanished. Perhaps in one or two of these *interglacial* stages, as we call them, the ice lingered vestigially in northern Canada. The last ice sheet, which attained its maximum about 20,000 years ago, did not disappear in northern Canada until about 6,000 years ago; and it may well be that the plateau icecaps of Baffin are its final relics. We have plain evidence that the interglacials were quite warm. At least one of them in eastern Canada was warmer than the present climate.

The usually accepted terminology for the Pleistocene events is shown in Table 2-1. The record may not be in its final form and several alternatives are possible, particularly in correlating widely separated areas.

The glacial ages in the North American column are all named for middle western states, for it is the magnificent series of glacial drifts south of the Great Lakes that has yielded the clues to the Pleistocene chronology. So far, there has been little chance in Canada of emulating the results of the American geologists. Near the centre of a region of glaciation, almost all visible features of the landscape are the work of the most recent ice sheet, which naturally tends to destroy the work of its predecessors. In the Midwest, however, the ice was nearly spent: in many cases, the later ice sheets merely spread their debris on top of the till sheets of the older glaciations. Sometimes, well-developed soils and the remains of vegetation can still be distinguished on the upper surface of these buried layers. Furthermore, the advances of the ice sheets into the region south of the Great Lakes were not quite identical; it is possible to find areas where each of the last three sheets was the last to invade, the subsequent sheets failing to reach the district. The Nebraskan drift, however, can usually be seen only where erosion has stripped away the younger layers.

Leverett, Chamberlain, and an army of later geologists have painstakingly worked out the succession of events by a scrutiny of the drift sheets in many different areas. They have adopted several criteria, of which the most valuable are these five: (1) the depth of weathering of the till sheets, which is very great upon the oldest tills but which has hardly begun on the latest sheet of all; (2) the presence of old soils between two sheets of till; (3) the presence of true interglacial beds between two sheets of till, especially loess (wind-deposited silt) or lake sediments; (4) the extent of erosion of the successive sheets, and especially the extent to which its morainic relief has been obliterated; and (5) the relations between each sheet of till and terminal moraines.

Although it has not been possible to show how many glaciations there were in Canada, if the ice sheets advanced *into* the United States on several occasions, then there were probably several glaciations here as well. There are interglacial deposits in many places (particularly in the Prairies), but so far it has not been proved that all the pre-Wisconsin glacial periods are represented. The last expansion of the Wisconsin glacier did its work too well, at least in the south. In the North, it may be different; for recent studies on Banks and Victoria islands suggest that the complex picture produced by several glaciations found in the Midwest of the United States on the south of the ice sheet may be repeated on what was the north side of the ice.

We must look at this final episode more closely. It is the only glaciation whose course we can fully reconstruct. When we have done this, we can look at some of the evidence for earlier glaciation with a heightened critical faculty.

The Final (Wisconsin) Glaciation

As the mild, interglacial Sangamon age drew to a close, and the harshening of the Canadian climate could no longer be denied, the Canadian landscape was different in several particulars from that of today. It is doubtful, for example, whether Hudson Bay existed. It occupies a shallow depression that was partly created in the outer crust by the weight of the Wisconsin ice, and it may largely disappear in a few tens of thousands of years. The preceding (Illinoian) ice sheet likewise depressed the crust; and it seems certain that the Sangamon interglacial, many times longer than the postglacial period, would have elevated and drained the older Hudson Bay. It is quite likely, though, that lakes still persisted in the region of the modern Great Lakes, for in several places the Wisconsin drift rests directly on lake sediments.

As the winters grew longer and the snowfall heavier (we believe the glacial ages to have been stormy), the snow began to outlast the summer melt in the mountains and uplands of Baffin Island. The same thing was probably happening in the Western Cordillera, particularly on the west slopes and summits of the Coast Range and the Rockies. A fall in *summer* temperature of 6°–7°F would be sufficient for glaciers to cover the greater part of Baffin Island. A further small decrease in temperature would enable ice sheets to form on much of the plateau of northern Labrador–Quebec. Once the ice sheet reached a certain size, it was probably self-generating, cooling the local climate sufficiently to hasten its own expansion and to create adjacent icecaps with which it later amalgamated. Although our chronology is at best a rough estimate, only a few thousand years may have elapsed between the initial growth in Baffin Island and the time when the margin moved into the United States.

Ultimately a single ice sheet, which has

been called the Laurentide ice sheet, covered the whole of Canada east of the Rocky Mountains. The edge of the ice lay on the continental shelf southeast of Nova Scotia. The northern margin was roughly along Parry Channel, the great strait that links the Arctic Ocean and Baffin Bay.

The Wisconsin Laurentide ice sheet seems to have had a maximum thickness of about 2 miles. It was able to move radially outward from its centre of accumulation, surmounting any obstacle in its path. Most of the striated rock faces, till sheets, drumlins, eskers, and moraines of eastern and central Canada are its handiwork. During the late stages, it became much shallower; and the outer margins, no longer able to surmount the mountains in its path, were deflected into lobes that followed the main valley routes, such as the upper St. Lawrence, the Champlain Valley of New York, and the floor of the Gulf of St. Lawrence. But at its thickest, it seems to have surmounted the highest peaks of the Canadian Shield, the Adirondacks, and the Appalachian–Acadian highlands (including Gaspé). The Cypress Hills in the southern Saskatchewan prairies may have projected as a nunatak.

This view has not always held, and there are still those who reject it. At various times, it has been claimed that nunataks existed in the Shickshock Mountains of Gaspé, the Long Range of Newfoundland, and the Torngat Mountains of northern Labrador, and that they acted as refuges for arctic-alpine plants at the height of glaciation. It is now thought that these summits were indeed clear of ice towards the close of the Wisconsin, but it is probable—and in some cases certain—that they were submerged when the ice was at its maximum thickness.

In the western mountains, there developed an entirely different Wisconsin glacier, the Cordilleran ice sheet. Today, if one stands on an existing glacier in the Rockies, one can much more easily visualize the Cordilleran ice sheet than comprehend the Laurentide icecap. It was not until 1926, however, that the previous existence of a continuous Cor-

dilleran ice sheet was confirmed, in a report on the Cariboo and Cassiar districts of British Columbia published by W. A. Johnston. Before that time, most researchers visualized a great expansion of the valley glaciers and of the coalescent masses we call piedmont glaciers. As late as 1919, J. B. Tyrell wrote that he was sure that the interior plateaus were unglaciated. But it was left to Johnston to prove that, at its climax, the ice had buried the entire Western Cordillera from Coast Range to Rockies, forming a true ice sheet. Since that date, we have, if anything, increased our estimates of its size. We think of it as a huge mass of confluent alpine glaciers, lying almost motionless between the two great bounding mountain chains. At its maximum, the Cordilleran glacier was not unlike the Greenland ice sheet of today: a vast, thick, and probably slow-moving body of inland ice, discharging to the sea through the deep valleys of the Coast Range and the northwest United States, and meeting, east of the Rockies, the Laurentide ice.

The ice did not spread far south of the international boundary. Widespread glaciers of the alpine type, vastly greater than those of today, covered the high ranges of the western United States; but much of the plateau country between the Coast Range or Cascades on the west and the Rockies on the east was very lightly glaciated or free of ice, and the true Cordilleran ice sheet barely attained a line 100 miles south of the 49th parallel. The northern margin of the ice sheet was also feebly developed, probably because of lack of snow. Tongues of ice from the ice sheet to the south crept northwards along the deep valleys of the Yukon, and the great alpine glaciers of the St. Elias Range were greater than they are today; but many parts of the northern Yukon seem to have escaped glaciation altogether—as they did, indeed, in all the previous glaciations (Fig. 2-2).

On the north side, the Laurentide Ice Sheet failed to cross Parry Channel, except possibly at a single point in the west. For more than half a century, there has been disagreement as to whether or not the islands farther

Fig. 2-2 Nunataks and unglaciated areas in the Pleistocene period:
areas not covered by ice at the
height of the last glaciation about
18,000 years ago. Many more nunataks probably existed; those indicated are conjectured.

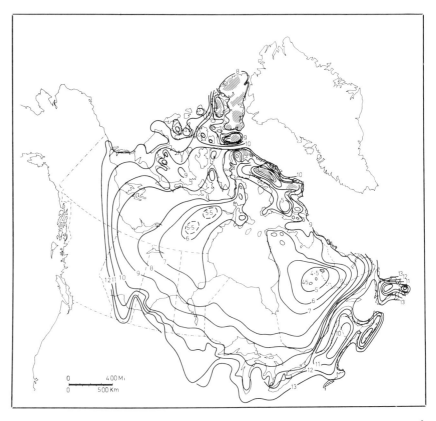

Fig. 2-3 Retreat of the Laurentide and Innuitian (Archipelago) ice sheets in 10^3
years B.P. (after Bryson, Wendland, Ives, and Andrews)

north were covered with ice. It is probable that each island was covered with a shallow ice dome, perhaps not more than a few hundred feet thick. The ice in the domes was stagnant or moved imperceptibly, while more mobile ice occupied the channels between the islands. The whole ice sheet over the northern Arctic islands is called the Innuitian.

The Laurentide ice was, however, by far the most extensive of this period, and it is to the fluctuations of it that we must return. We have seen that the Wisconsin ice began to advance about 70,000 years ago. A deep-freeze followed, lasting for at least 20,000 years, during which the southern ice margin was principally in the United States (there were almost certainly somewhat warmer periods when southern Canada was free of ice, but the region probably continued to experience an arctic climate). There followed perhaps 15,000–25,000 years of cold climate, when the ice margin fluctuated across southern Canada, occasionally reaching into the United States. Then, between 35,000 and 25,000 years ago, the ice began to advance again, reaching its extreme maximum nearly 20,000 years ago. From that time onwards, although there were occasionally temporary readvances, the ice margin retreated (Fig. 2-3); and 6,000 years ago the Ice Age ended, except on the upland of Baffin Island.

It must now be clear that the Wisconsin glaciation was far from being the simple advance and retreat of an icecap. It was, in fact, extremely complex; and there is little doubt that many of its intricacies, particularly of the early stages, are still only partly understood.

The Older Glaciations

As we have already said, the late Wisconsin ice so effectively scraped the surface of Canada that the landscape bears few traces of the earlier glaciations. But we accept the verdict of United States researchers that there were several glacial ages, and that in each a great Canadian glacier-complex overwhelmed the northern part of their country. We suppose,

with good reason, that these glaciers were very like the Wisconsin ice sheets, forming over the same areas and passing through a similar cycle of development.

Continued investigation has shown that interglacial beds, often sandwiched between glacial tills, are present in many parts of the country—although, because they outcrop only sporadically, correlation has proved difficult. Probably the finest exposures are in the bluffs along the north shores of lakes Erie and Ontario. The citizens of Toronto (although little aware of it) build their homes upon a great thickness of glacial drift that contains an extraordinarily rich record of the past. The Toronto deposits were first described in 1878 and were subsequently made famous by the long study and interest of A. P. Coleman, for many years a professor of geology at the University of Toronto.

The succession is exposed in the cliffs of Lake Ontario, particularly near Scarborough Bluffs; and there are even more important exposures in brickworks in the Don Valley. The record is summed up in the table on page 32 and further illustrated in Fig. 2-4.[1]

The basal till is obviously a glacial sediment; and, although it is very thin, it is clearly a deposit of an early glacier that flowed out from the Lake Ontario basin. Above there is a considerable thickness of lacustrine sediments, which Coleman called the Toronto Formation. The lower member, the Don beds, is comprised of interglacial sands, clays, and gravel that were deposited in a lake with a shoreline about 60 feet higher than Lake Ontario. These beds have yielded an astonishing rich fossil record, telling of a warm climate that persisted for thousands of years. Many tree-trunks were washed into the lake, and a host of leaves was imprisoned between layers of mud. A rich deciduous forest covered the nearby lakeshore, a forest richer in species than its present-day equivalent. The climate seems to have been 4°–5° warmer in summer than it is today, resembling that of southern Illinois. Among the trees that have been

---

[1] Taken from J. Terasmae, *Geological Survey of Canada Bulletin*, 56, 1960.

Lake Iroquois sand	Lacustrine sediments	Lake Iroquois phase
Leaside till	Sandy till	Port Huron glaciation
Thorncliffe beds	Stratified sands and varved clays	Interglacial
Danforth beds	Till, varved clay, sand, and peat	Fluctuating ice margin
Sunnybrook till	Silt till	
	Unconformity	
Scarborough beds	Stratified sand, stratified silty sand	St. Pierre interstadial (?)
	Unconformity	Glaciation (?)
Don beds	Stratified sand and gravel	Sangamon interglacial
	Unconformity	
York till	Clay till	Illinoian (?)
	Unconformity	
	Bedrock	

identified, there were four species of maple, three of ash, six of oak, and two of poplar. There were such odd visitors to southern Ontario as the osage orange (*Madura pomifera*), now a native of the far southwest of the United States, and the black locust, banished today to the southern Appalachians (though it is still hardy locally, if grown in gardens). The lake in whose sediments these trees were imprisoned was rich, moreover, in clams of a kind common in the Mississippi Valley. Coleman considered the Don beds to be of Yarmouth age, but they are now believed to date from the Sangamon interglacial.

The succeeding Scarborough beds are also lacustrine and their deposition was separated from the Don beds by a period when ice either approached or covered the Toronto district. They have yielded an abundance (72 species) of beetles, nearly all now extinct. The climate was boreal (with a coniferous forest) during most of the interval, although beginning and ending with subarctic conditions. The mean temperature may have been 10°F cooler than at present, and a correlation with the St. Pierre interval (see below) has been suggested. The Scarborough beds are overlain by a succession of tills, and by varved clays deposited in lakes marginal to ice. They probably represent a long period of successive ice advances and retreats across southern Ontario. These in turn are covered by deposits of Lake Iroquois, the last of a long series of glacial lakes.

A varied group of sediments has been examined by Dreimanis on the north shore of Lake Erie. It also shows glacial stages separated by warmer periods. Dreimanis believes that they are a record of the mid-Wisconsin interstadials (warm oscillations)—the Port Talbot, occurring between 45,000 and 50,000 years ago; and the Plum Point interstadial, occurring 25,000–30,000 years ago. On both occasions, temperatures were probably somewhat cooler than they are today.

In other parts of Canada, there are so-called interglacial beds that in most cases probably date from interstadials in the early part of Wisconsin time. They include the St. Pierre deposits found between Lake St. Peter and Quebec City, which were formed about 65,000 years ago over a period of perhaps 6,000–7,000 years, at a temperature that at its warmest was 3°–5°F lower than it is today. Other interstadial deposits of a similar age have been found along the Missinaibi River in northern Ontario.

Much the same is true of western Canada.

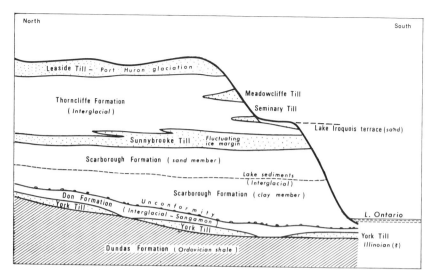

Fig. 2-4   Changes of environmental conditions in the Pleistocene period shown by sediments in southern Ontario (after Karrow)

The Prairies are covered by a deep mantle of drift that contains the debris of earlier ice advances. E. A. Christiansen described three distinct tills in southern Saskatchewan, chiefly near the Missouri Coteau, of proven Wisconsin age. The upper till was separated from the middle by a thin, discontinuous spread of sediments containing some shells and spruce fragments, indicating a climate like that of northern Saskatchewan today. Wickenden, who first discussed these deposits, could not decide whether this represented a true interglacial age, or whether it had come into being during the retreat of the Wisconsin ice, which later overwhelmed the region during a temporary readvance. It is now thought to be interstadial. Between the middle and lower tills is a thicker intervening layer. It rests upon a deeply weathered and eroded lower till and probably represents the sediments deposited in a proglacial lake during the retreat of the ice. The best exposures described are near Swift Current.

The Cordilleran glacier also came and went more than once, but we have exasperatingly little clear evidence. W. A. Johnston discovered two tills in the Cariboo region of interior British Columbia, separated by pay-streaks of gold-bearing, oxidized, and cemented gravels. The lower till has been subjected to prolonged weathering and erosion. In the lower Fraser Valley and on Vancouver Island are non-glacial sediments, known as the Quadra series, that are overlain by till. They probably represent a long interstadial during which temperatures were somewhat cooler than they are today, possibly in the middle Wisconsin. There is also strong radiocarbon evidence for non-glacial deposits of considerably greater age.

Selected Readings

Bird, J. B., *The Physiography of Arctic Canada*, Baltimore, The Johns Hopkins Press, 1967, Ch. VIII, pp. 89–116.

Blake, W., Jr., "End Moraines and Deglaciation Chronology in Northern Canada", *Geol. Surv. Can. Paper* 66-26, 1966, 31 pp.

Chapman, L. J., and D. F. Putnam, *The Physiography of Southern Ontario*, Toronto, University of Toronto Press, 1966, 386 pp.

Flint, R. F., *Glacial and Quaternary Geology*, New York, Wiley, 1971, 892 pp.

Prest, V. K., "Retreat of Wisconsin and Recent Ice in North America", *Geol. Surv. Can. Map* 1257A, 1968.
Quaternary Geology of Canada in Douglas, R. J. W. (ed.), *Geology and Economic Minerals of Canada*, Ottawa, Queen's Printer, 1971, pp. 676–764.

Sharp, R. P., *Glaciers*, Eugene, University of Oregon Press, 1960, 78 pp.

3

The Scenery of the Glaciations

We have seen that both continental and alpine glaciers move slowly but inexorably, for ice is plastic under the high pressures produced by its own weight. Continental glaciers move radially outwards; and when they are thick, to a considerable degree they act independently of the relief of the land they bury. Alpine glaciers move faster but are constrained to follow pre-existing stream valleys. The bottoms of glaciers become charged with rock fragments or boulders; a slowly sliding mass of ice, armed with such tools and impelled by the weight of the column of purer ice above, performs striking feats of erosion. The steep-sided fiords of coastal British Columbia, with walls sometimes rising 3,000 feet above the sea and plunging 2,000 feet below it, were carved out of the massive granites of the Coast Range by extensions of the glaciers that discharge into their heads today. Much of Canada bears the tool-marks of glacial erosion.

The eroded material, varying in size from the finest "rock-flour" to boulders the size of houses, is carried along by the ice towards the margins. Ultimately, this material is deposited, either directly by the ice when it melts (*glacial drift*) or else in straggling areas of outwash sands and gravels carried beyond the margin of the ice by the melt waters. In addition to the landforms caused by glacial erosion, then, we have to consider those formed through deposition. Patches of glacial drift are scattered over almost the entire surface of continental Canada.

The influence of ice on the preglacial scenery depends to a considerable extent on the pre-existing relief. Where the landscape is mountainous, the valleys are deep and the gradients steep, and the glaciers are con-

strained and flow relatively rapidly—although this may mean no more than a few feet a day. Unless the ice is very thick, the highest peaks will not be buried; and it is this combination of glacier streams and exposed summits that comprises *mountain glaciation*. Where the relief is slight, the motion of the ice is normally very slow—perhaps no greater than a yard a year. In the absence of high ice velocities and with all the terrain protected from extra-glacial weathering, the changes resulting from *continental glaciation* are not as rapid and, in most cases, are less striking than those of mountain glaciation.

Mountain areas that have been glaciated are normally much modified from their preglacial condition (Fig. 3-1). The valleys that formerly were V-shaped are often deepened and widened along the floor; with the erosion and destruction of spurs, the valleys become U-shaped. The tributary valleys to the main valleys are not deepened as quickly. Consequently, when the ice melts, they are left hanging above the main valley and their streams plunge down from them, often in spectacular waterfalls. In the Western Cordillera, U-shaped glaciated valleys are found in many areas; but perhaps the best example is the Yoho Valley, with its magnificent waterfalls, hanging valleys, and benches marking the position of the preglacial valley before it was over-deepened. In eastern Canada, mountain glaciers never existed or were present for only a short time, and the characteristic scenery is not found south of the Arctic. In Labrador and farther north, mountain glaciation was, and in many areas still is, a potent force in the landscape; and the spectacular coastal scenery of eastern Baffin Island, where many of the larger valleys are

A. Before glaciation sets in, the region has smoothly rounded divides and narrow, V-shaped stream valleys.

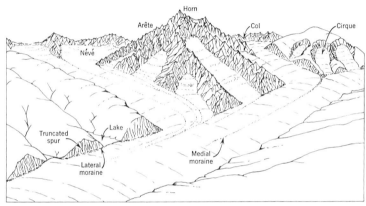

B. After glaciation has been in progress for thousands of years new erosional forms are developed.

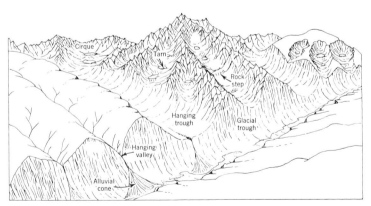

C. With the disappearance of the ice a system of glacial troughs is exposed.

Fig. 3-1   Evolution of glacial landforms: a highland zone is illustrated before, during, and after glaciation (prepared by Strahler from diagrams by W. M. Davis and A. K. Lobeck)

Plate 3-1   A pyramidical peak or horn, with cirques at the base: Mt. Assiniboine, B.C. (British Columbia Government Photograph.)

drowned to form fiords, is a consequence of it.

Over-deepening of the valleys is rarely uniform; and when the ice melts, rock basins and bars across the valley are often preserved. Lake Waterton in southern Alberta is a case in point: a great rock bar, which overlooks the foothills of the Rockies to the east, cuts across its mouth.

When mountains have been only partly glaciated, small glaciers accumulate in hollows on the sides of the mountains. Gradually, through grinding and weathering, these hollows are enlarged and cut back into deep basins with vertical sides often rising to several thousand feet. Where a number of *cirque glaciers*, as this type is called, develop on one mountain-side, the sides of the mountain are steepened and eventually it becomes a pyramid or *horn*, with its adjacent cirques separated only by knife-edged *arêtes*. The most famous is perhaps the Matterhorn, but pyramidical peaks are common in practically all mountain ranges. Mount Assiniboine is an outstanding example in the Rockies.

Other cirques may form at the upper end of a glaciated valley, where a basin is separated by a lip from the main valley. At different phases of the glaciation, some or all of these features may be occupied by ice. This can be seen clearly near the Columbia Ice Field, from which glaciers descend into the valleys of British Columbia and Alberta. On the east side, the longest are the Saskatchewan Glacier, which descends 5,900 feet from the ice field over a distance of 5½ miles; and the better-known Athabasca Glacier, which reaches almost to the Banff–Jasper highway. During the last hundred years, the Athabasca Glacier has retreated about four-fifths of a mile and (in some ways equally impressive) the ice surface has lowered over much of its length by about 100 feet. In the past decade, the termini have retreated at a rate of 65–80 feet per year. Table 3-1 shows the fluctuations of some of the major glaciers in the Rockies.

The Dome Glacier, adjacent to the Athabasca Glacier, was at one time a true outlet glacier. But with today's climatic amelioration, it now receives little ice from the plateau and is more strictly a valley-head cirque glacier.

Cirques are rare in southeastern Canada; a few were formed in Gaspé, around the Cape Breton Highlands, and in northern Newfoundland. But although mountain gla-

TABLE 3-1
FLUCTUATIONS OF GLACIERS
IN THE ROCKY MOUNTAINS

Glacier	Beginning date of recession	Rate of retreat in second quarter of twentieth century
Angel (Mt. Edith Cavell)	1733	–
Saskatchewan	1854 (1st max.) 1893 (2nd max.)	114 ft./yr.
Athabasca	1731	87 ft./yr.
Dome	1875	31 ft./yr.
Yoho	1855	150 ft./yr.

ciation was unimportant in eastern Canada, cirques, arêtes, and valley moraines are widespread in the White Mountains of New Hampshire. These mountains are 2,000–3,000 feet higher than the Canadian Appalachians, and this seems to have been just enough for them to support cirque glaciers in the cool period preceding continental glaciation.

Many valley glaciers carry the eroded debris away from the mountains, often as far as the sea, as they must have done off the coasts of British Columbia and Baffin Island. Where the glaciers are not as large and where, during retreat, the snouts of the glaciers are in the valleys, debris is either carried out in front by streams to form an outwash plain or left as ridges or piles of glacial drift across the valley or on its sides. These deposits are *terminal and lateral moraines*, and they are often a conspicuous feature of a glaciated valley. In areas where there is still some glacier ice, the final moraine is often close up against the ice. Changes in the ice front in the past century, which in western Canada has been primarily one of retreat, have left several parallel moraines roughly concentric to the ice margin. This can be seen clearly near the terminus of the Athabasca Glacier, where the Banff–Jasper highway cuts through the outer moraines.

The landforms of continental glaciation, particularly those of deposition, resemble in detail many landforms of mountain glaciation; but when they are seen as a group, the overall effect is often very different. As in our discussion of mountain glaciation, let us start with erosional landforms.

The simplest form of erosion by ice sheets consists simply of the stripping of loose soil and subsoil, leaving the bare rock surface fully exposed. The accompanying grinding, abrasive action was very general in eastern Canada, although it is doubtful that it planed off more than a few tens of feet of rock; the widely held view that the flatness of the Canadian Shield is due to glacial erosion is certainly untrue. Great areas of the Shield, as well as of the hillier parts of Appalachian Canada, nevertheless show this coarsened, abraded surface, which often bears scratches (called *striae*) and grooves as witness of the direction of ice movement. Similar striated surfaces can often be found beneath the layers of glacial debris in other areas. Even so, the erosive ability of the ice was very variable; and at many places in the Canadian Shield, around its southern edge, and in Nova Scotia, preglacial soils were undisturbed by the ice.

In the crystalline areas of the Shield, preglacial weathering and erosion were controlled largely by joint and fault patterns, which usually intersect at right angles. The ice removed the associated debris, leaving in many areas narrow shallow valleys and basins of uneven depth. Today these are filled with water, and form straight-sided lakes whose shorelines are often cruciform in pattern or follow sharp bends.

Another effect of continental ice that we can identify in the hilly areas goes by the homely term *stoss and lee relief*. In these areas the individual hills or rock outcrops have fairly gentle slopes on the flank *facing* the oncoming glacier (the stoss slope), whereas the lee flank is steep, craggy, and abrupt in profile. This asymmetry extends from small rocks a few yards across (known as *roches moutonnées*) to large hills some hundreds of feet high. The reverse effect occurs where

Plate 3-2   An alpine landscape in Baffin Island that has experienced mountain glaciation for tens of thousands and possibly hundreds of thousands of years. Cirque and valley glaciers, cirques, arêtes, pyramidical peaks, glaciated troughs, hanging valleys, and a fiord are conspicuous in the picture. (National Air Photo Library, Surveys and Mapping Branch, Department of Energy, Mines and Resources. Photo T326R-76.)

there has been deposition of glacial material down-ice from a rock knob; here it has a "crag and tail" form.

A careful plotting of all the striae from a region, together with an analysis of the stoss and lee effect, gives an indication of the direction of glacier flow. It is by this device, in fact, that we have slowly crystallized our views about the form of the ancient ice sheets, and the dispersal centres from which they radiated. Unfortunately, such evidence is rarely conclusive. All too often, we find more than one set of striae, sometimes bearing witness to several distinct glaciations, sometimes indicating merely a shift in the direction of movement during a single glaciation.

Deposits of glacial drift are highly distinctive in relief and in composition. We can distinguish very roughly between two classes of drift: *till*, which is unsorted in size, containing fragments ranging from fine silt or clay to giant boulders; and *stratified drift*, showing the characteristic sorted, layered appearance of water-laid sediments. The former class owes its apparently structureless form to its origin as a deposit from the ice itself, either at the glacier's base, or else from the mass as a whole when the sheet melted. Stratified drift consists of material washed together by melt water along the ice margin. If till is examined carefully, it is seen to consist largely of ground-up material derived locally from the solid bedrock beneath; this is often as true of the boulders, cobbles, and pebbles as it is of the finer-grained material making up the bulk of the till. Occasionally, however, there are far-travelled boulders (erratics) which are plainly foreign to the local region. The fields around Montreal, for example, abound in boulders from the Canadian Shield to the

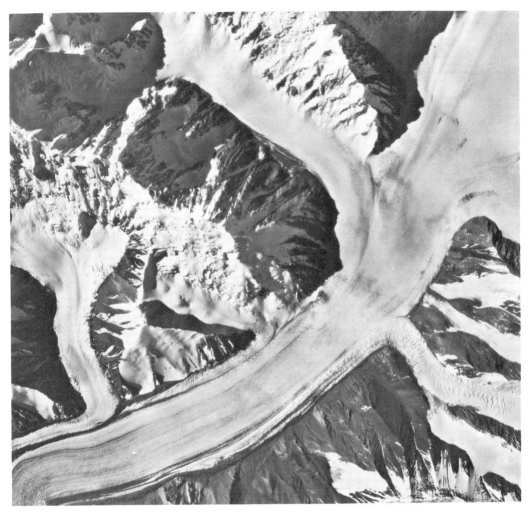

Plate 3-3   A large valley glacier flowing through the mountains on the Alaska–Yukon border is joined by several tributary glaciers between the accumulation (top right of picture) and ablation zones. (National Air Photo Library, Surveys and Mapping Branch, Department of Energy, Mines and Resources. Photo A21523-4.)

north; and rocks torn from the Laurentides north of Quebec have been picked up near Cincinnati.

When a continental ice sheet finally retreats from an area, it usually leaves a deposit of the debris that it has picked up. In general, the thickness varies with the resistance of the bedrock to the weathering processes. Thus, in eastern Canada, the drift cover, although variable, is rarely more than a few feet thick. Farther west, in southern Ontario, it is often several tens of feet thick where it has developed over shales; and in certain areas of the

Prairies, where it has been deposited on unconsolidated and semi-consolidated rocks, the cover may exceed several hundred feet.

Where the debris is thin, it may fail to cover the bedrock completely, a common occurrence in the Shield; but even when it is continuous, the shape of the bedrock surface controls the scenery. It is only when the till is deep that it produces an entirely new landscape (Fig. 3-2).

The surface of unmodified till may vary from a nearly flat terrain, perhaps broken only by narrow postglacial valleys—a type

Plate 3-4   Mountains in Baffin Island with cirque glaciers on the slopes. In the foreground, a terminal moraine left by a retreating glacier contains glacier ice (dark areas) buried by morainic debris.

Plate 3-5   Prairie mounds in the vicinity of Edmonton, Alberta. Similar low till domes of uncertain origin are found in several parts of western Canada.

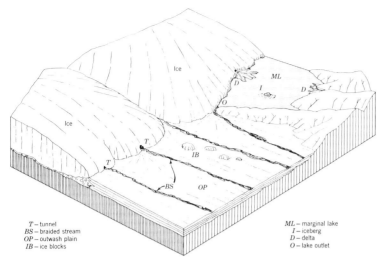

T – tunnel
BS – braided stream
OP – outwash plain
IB – ice blocks

ML – marginal lake
I – iceberg
D – delta
O – lake outlet

A. With the ice front stabilized and the ice in a wasting, stagnant condition, various depositional features are built by meltwaters.

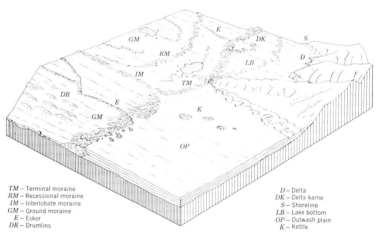

TM – Terminal moraine
RM – Recessional moraine
IM – Interlobate moraine
GM – Ground moraine
E – Esker
DR – Drumlins

D – Delta
DK – Delta kame
S – Shoreline
LB – Lake bottom
OP – Outwash plain
K – Kettle

B. After the ice has wasted completely away, a variety of new landforms made under the ice is exposed to view.

Fig. 3-2   Marginal landforms of continental glaciers (after Strahler)

that is well developed northwest of Toronto in the vicinity of Malton—to major irregularities that are quite properly called hills. Probably the most representative till plain is *gently undulating ground moraine.* It is often extremely monotonous, for the till is more than 50 feet thick and buries the underlying rock. The local relief is no more than 10–15 feet. When seen from the ground, the low surface appears completely patternless; but from the air, it can often be seen that the surface is comprised of ridges and depressions. In the Prairies, the depressions contain sloughs, and often aspen and low bushes. These depressions may be the result of uneven deposition of till—although in some areas, where they are circular, they apparently result from the melting of ice blocks that were initially in the till. The plain in Manitoba between Minnedosa and the Trans-Canada Highway is an exceptionally good example; indeed, when viewed from the air,

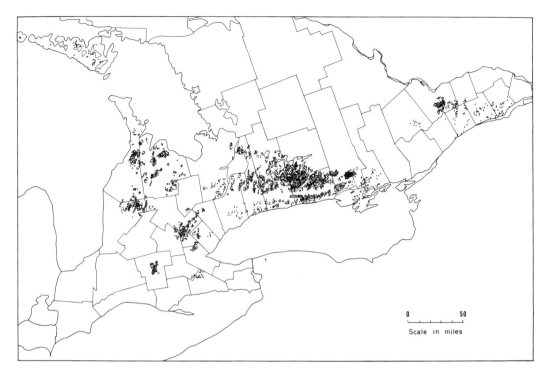

Fig. 3-3   Drumlin fields in southern Ontario (after Chapman and Putnam)

this type of terrain can be recognized in many parts of the Prairies, particularly in central Alberta, southeast of Edmonton.

In some areas, undulating ground moraine is replaced by far more irregular terrain, in which there are isolated *drift knobs, moraine plateaus*, fairly deep *kettles*, and sandy *kame ridges*. This terrain is referred to as *hummocky ground moraine*, and the local relief may reach 50 feet or more. It is believed to result from the slow disintegration of stagnant ice which contained considerable moraine in its lower layers.

Both these types of moraine are essentially patternless. In contrast, in some areas the till has been moulded into long, low, parallel ridges, often only a few feet high and separated by elongated shallow depressions. These features are variously referred to as *fluting* or *drumlinoids*. The long axes of the ridges are parallel to the direction of ice movement. Although drumlinoids often control local soils and drainage, and in some areas vegetation, they are almost invisible at ground level;

thus, they were seldom recognized before the introduction of aerial photography. They are widely distributed in the Prairies and in Arctic Canada, particularly west of Hudson Bay, and have a somewhat more restricted distribution in southwestern Ontario, central British Columbia, and the Maritime Provinces.

In some localities the drumlinoids are higher and oval in plan, with a profile not unlike an upturned boat. Characteristically, they are about 50 feet high, but they may exceed 300 feet. In this form, they are known as *drumlins*, a term borrowed by the geomorphologist from the Gaelic *drum* meaning a hill. Drumlins normally occur in fields, in which they number several hundreds. By far the best known is the astonishing field of southern Ontario (Fig. 3-3) and nearby New York State, described in the works of H. L. Fairchild (south of Lake Ontario) and L. J. Chapman and D. F. Putnam (to the north). There are 15,000–20,000 drumlins in this field, and many more have been destroyed by

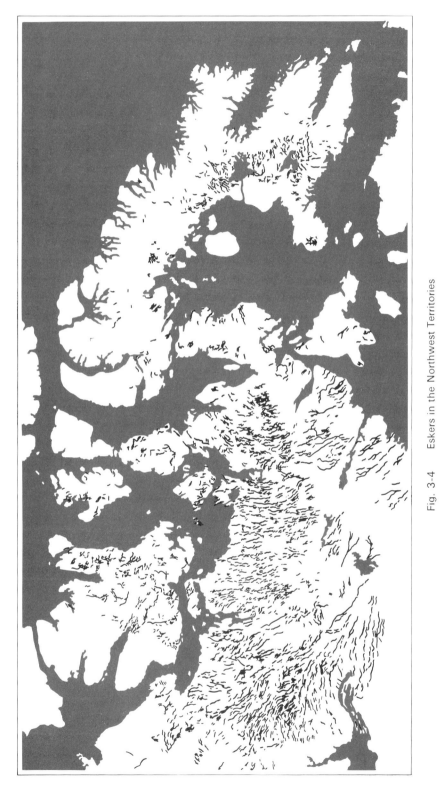

Fig. 3-4   Eskers in the Northwest Territories

Plate 3-6   An esker, rising nearly 100 feet above a lake, crosses the Barren Grounds: Coñtwoyto Lake, District of Mackenzie, N.W.T.

the waves of the Great Lakes. They can be seen very clearly in the southwest end of Rice Lake (Ontario), where they are partly submerged to form islands. The south-central Ontario field reaches its finest development between Rice Lake and Peterborough. Another spectacular drumlin field is in Nova Scotia around Lunenburg. The town is built on drumlins, and the harbour has several drumlin islands. Other drumlins in the same field are partly submerged to form the many islands in Mahone Bay off Chester. Rather surprisingly, there are no large drumlin fields in the Prairies, although there are small groups—notably around Dollard, Saskatchewan.

Till plains, particularly in their flatter parts, were modified during the final stages of the ice retreat, when gravel ridges that are believed to represent crevasse fillings were deposited, or small moraine ridges were formed at the ice front. It is not unusual to find that

glacial lakes or seas have washed the fines from the higher parts of the plain, leaving boulder deposits, while the fines have been redeposited in the hollows.

Sinuous, sandy ridges stretching for miles in some consistent direction and 10–30 feet high (although in some areas they exceed 100 feet) are a characteristic landform of continental glaciation. They are usually comprised of sands and gravels, which are often stratified and show signs of tumultuous, shifting flow in the water that laid them down. Such ridges, called *eskers*, are believed to mark the courses of melt-water rivers whose former channels were on, in, and under the ice. Where they flowed in tunnels, such rivers could form natural siphons and could flow uphill for a limited distance. Accordingly, the eskers that mark their courses may sometimes ignore the valleys of the modern landscape; they often ascend low ridges and heights of land. Being sandy, and hence dry, they are favourite trackways for the beasts of the forests, and man sometimes uses them for his roads and railways. Eskers are found in almost all glaciated areas, notably in southern Canada in the Eastern Townships of Quebec and in several parts of southern Ontario. They reach their greatest development in the northern Canadian Shield, where individual eskers, interrupted only by rivers and lakes, extend in some cases for several hundred miles (Fig. 3-4). When the eskers of a large area are plotted on a map, they often show a dendritic pattern of tributaries that is the image of the vast melt-water river systems that formed them.

So far, we have been discussing the deposits formed beneath the glacier itself. Another group of landforms formed along the glacier margin includes *terminal moraines*, *kame moraines*, *kames*, and *outwash fans*.

The outer edge of a glacier marks the line along which melting is just able to keep pace with the ice advances. As the ice melts, it dumps its load, forming a confused mass of coarse, ill-sorted material called a *terminal moraine* or *end moraine*. If the ice remains at one position for a long period of years, this moraine becomes thick, and remains as a conspicuous ridge when the ice retires. Such lumpy, boulder-strewn ridges raise their irregular profiles in many areas (Fig. 3-5). In detail, we can distinguish three sub-classes of major terminal moraine. If the glacier remains stationary for many years, much of the material accumulated along its margin is actually deposited by melt water, and is roughly stratified; such a deposit is a *kame moraine*. In Quebec, the western part of the St. Narcisse moraine from the St. Maurice River to the Laurentians and the moraines along the northeast side of the Canadian Appalachians are primarily kame moraines. Many moraines are dominated by, and appear to consist of, material shoved up by the advance of the glacier, as well as material let down by surface melting. These are called *till moraines*. The Tiger Hills moraine of southwestern Manitoba and the core of the Oak Ridges moraine in southern Ontario are of this type.

Most terminal moraines, however, are a combination of kame deposits and till.

When glacier ice advances into semi-consolidated sediments that are frozen, the ice may push up the sediments into faulted blocks, producing hills tens and even hundreds of feet high. *Push moraines* of this type are forming at the snouts of advancing glaciers in the high Arctic at the present time. During the Pleistocene glaciation, western Canada seems to have been colder than the east of the country, for this is where push moraines are found. Herschel Island near the borders of the Yukon and Alaska was thrust up in this way at the extreme northwestern limit of the Laurentide ice sheet; in the Prairies, several isolated hill masses—notably the Neutral Hills in Alberta—were formed in this way. It is extremely probable that the low, preglacial escarpment known in Saskatchewan as the Missouri Coteau was pushed into by the glacier and the relief thus magnified.

A different type of moraine for a long time escaped attention because it is far smaller than an end moraine. These *minor moraines*, generally formed of bouldery till, occur in fields of low sub-parallel ridges 1 to 10 feet high, are up to a mile in length, and are separated by distances of 25–100 yards. In many cases, they appear to have been formed, perhaps annually, at an ice front that was calving into water. Although they are found throughout mainland Canada, they probably reach their finest development in the Prairies and on the east side of Hudson Bay. Often they are not recognized on the ground until they have been identified first from the air.

When the major end moraines are considered in conjunction with the flow patterns visible in the ice or deduced from drumlinoids and striae, it often becomes possible to reconstruct the shape of the ice sheet during the retreat phase.

We have seen already that *kames* are banks of sand and gravel, often very ill sorted, deposited along the ice margin. The same term is used for coarse-grained material left on the ice by streams, which may originate on the

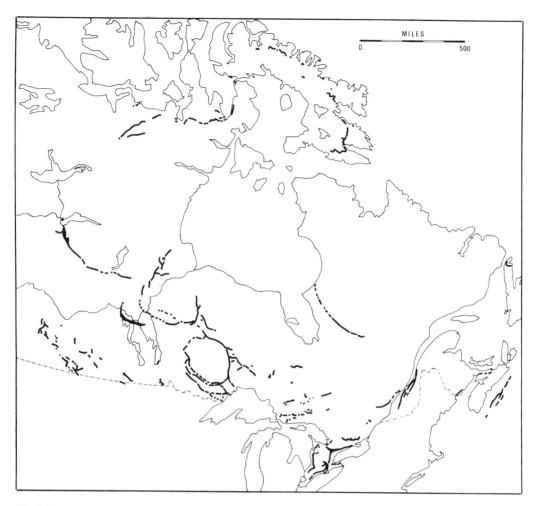

Fig. 3-5   End moraines in eastern and central Canada (modified after Geological Survey of Canada)

unglaciated land beyond the ice front. When the ice retreats, they are left as irregular sandy hills; or where the sediment has been trapped between a glacier and the valley side, as was the case in many of the interior valleys of southern British Columbia, it may have a roughly flat, gently sloping upper surface known as a *kame terrace*. Kame moraines are often formed where continental ice pushes up against, but not over, a line of hills. The kames in the passes of the Canadian Appalachians in southeastern Quebec and rather similar ones on the north side of the Cobequid Hills in Nova Scotia are of this type.

Outwash fans are the fan-shaped deltas of glacial melt-water streams formed as the water spreads out beyond the terminal moraine. The vast quantity of debris presented to these streams is usually so great that the valleys of the streams become choked with sand and gravel terraces for tens or even hundreds of miles beyond the ice front. Almost all valleys in mountains that have been glaciated have valley trains and associated terraces, and many valleys in areas of less relief have been similarly choked. The valleys in the southern Canadian Shield between Ottawa and Quebec are choked in this way with moraines, and outwash and related terraces, which combine to give the valleys relatively flat floors suitable for some farming and for the location of highways. Even more spectacular is the valley train of the Madawaska–Saint John River that extends from Lake Témiscouata in Quebec, with occasional breaks, for nearly 200 miles to below Fredericton, New Brunswick.

Particularly where the valley train is no longer confined, outwash fans coalesce to form extensive sandy plains, such as that which stretches from Lachute to the St. Maurice on the north side of the St. Lawrence or in Lotbinière County, southwest of Quebec. In the Maritimes, part of the Annapolis Valley is filled with outwash. Perhaps the largest outwash plain of all, and certainly one of the most striking, is in the Northwest Territories along the middle course of the Back River.

In case this gives the impression that glacial melt waters do nothing but deposit coarse sediments, it must be remembered that rushing water can also erode and that many channels which today are not occupied by water or which carry only undersized streams were fashioned by escaping glacial waters under or just beyond the ice. The numerous spillways of the southern Prairies illustrate this point well; but in fact, smaller and otherwise paradoxical channels can be found in all parts of the country.

Selected Readings

Embleton, C., and C. A. M. King, *Glacial and Periglacial Geomorphology*, New York, St. Martin's Press, 1968, 608 pp.

Strahler, A. N., *The Earth Sciences*, New York, Harper Row, 1971, Ch. 40 and 41, pp. 706–756.

Thornbury, W. D., *Principles of Geomorphology*, New York, Wiley, 1969, 594 pp.

4

The Glacial Lakes

As the great ice sheet covering Canada east of the Rockies began to retreat, extensive lakes developed at or near the front of the ice. At first, it seems rather odd that few glacial lakes existed at the maximum glaciation; but a map makes it obvious that major rivers drained away from the ice at that time, and there was less melt water then than later, when the great icecap was disappearing rapidly.

Small lakes dammed by glaciers have been known for a long time in Europe; Marjelen Sea on the side of the Aletsch Glacier is perhaps the best-known example. Only recently it has been discovered in northern Greenland and on Axel Heiberg and Ellesmere islands in northern Canada that proglacial lakes are extremely common along the sides of excessively cold glaciers. This is explained by the fact that most temperate valley glaciers are crevassed, and water passes through them into or under the ice, while cold glaciers are broken in this way only close to the surface.

The majority of the Pleistocene glacial lakes were formed when ice blocked preglacial valleys. Other lakes developed when the weight of the ice deformed the earth's crust sufficiently to raise the natural outlet so that water no longer drained across it, or did so only after a lake had developed. Good, though often very complex, examples of these crustal changes occurred at several localities in the late glacial history of the Great Lakes. Other examples include glacial lakes Ann and Vermont in the Lake Champlain Basin (almost entirely in New York State and Vermont). At the time of the glacial lakes, about 12,000 years ago, the Champlain Basin was depressed in the north, close to the Canadian border; in this case, the lake level was also raised by the ice barrier in the St. Lawrence Lowlands. In Mackenzie district, the basin of Great Bear Lake was depressed on the east side, and the lake consequently transgressed these shores, although it continued to drain to the west.

Other lakes were produced when valleys were dammed by moraines. While these are not strictly glacial lakes, it is clear that they are closely associated with the Ice Age. This type of lake is rather common in mountainous areas, and many examples have been found in British Columbia and Baffin Island.

When glacial lakes have vanished—either because the ice has retreated and the ice barrier has disappeared, or because the land has recovered its preglacial position—evidence of their former existence is often conspicuous in the present scenery. Sometimes beaches are left, perhaps backed by cliffs or lines of washed-out boulders. The bluffs and beaches of Lake Agassiz along the foot of the Manitoba Escarpment and the Lake Iroquois shoreline that curves through midtown Toronto are outstanding cases, and many lesser-known examples can be found throughout the Prairies and southern Ontario. In the deeper parts of the lakes, clays and silts, often laminated (or varved), were deposited and today these form extremely level clay plains; the flat plain of the old floor of Lake Regina, west of the city of Regina, is a conspicuous case. In shallow near-shore lake waters, sands were deposited, primarily as deltas. The sands in Norfolk County in southwestern Ontario were carried into glacial lakes Whittlesey and Warren. Several deltas remain from the western shores of glacial Lake Agassiz, particularly the great sand delta of the Assiniboine that extends from near Brandon to east of

Shilo, Manitoba.

Often the waters of the glacial lakes overflowed across cols and hill-spurs, cutting and deepening valleys that are now dry and abandoned. The Covey Hill channel around the north end of the Adirondacks on the borders of Quebec and New York State is a spillway formed by a river draining a glacial lake that lay to the west of the Adirondacks.

Glacial and Postglacial Lakes in Western Canada

In British Columbia, many glacial lakes developed in the Fraser Plateau and the Columbia Mountains. Because they were confined between high valley sides, they were generally long and narrow. In the southern part of the province, Lake Thompson was the last of several lakes that occupied the Merritt–Ashcroft–Kamloops region and were joined with Lake Penticton in the Okanagan Valley. They were apparently formed by an ice sheet in the interior plateau which was nourished by glaciers spreading out from the Coast and Monash mountains. Terraces, deltas built in the lakes, and melt-water channels cut by the

escaping waters are conspicuous features in many parts of these valleys. Farther north, larger lakes occupied the Prince George–Fort St. James and Peace River regions.

Major changes were produced in the scenery of the Prairies by glacial lakes as the margin of the east North American ice sheet retreated to the northeast. In its retreat, it effectively blocked the preglacial drainage that flowed to Hudson Bay. Since the relief of the Prairies is generally greater in the west than in the east, the older lakes in the areas first to be deglacierized in Alberta tended to be long and narrow, while those in Saskatchewan and particularly Manitoba were far more extensive, although—with the exception of Lake Agassiz—short-lived. In the foothills of Alberta, the proglacial lakes were small; one of the largest extended southwards from the Bow River at Calgary. On the plains in central and eastern Alberta, there were lakes centred around the major valleys; these included the North Saskatchewan (Lake Edmonton), the valley at Red Deer (Lake Red Deer), the Red Deer around Drumheller, and the Oldman Valley at Lethbridge. These lakes left little erosive or sedimentary evi-

Plate 4-1   A spillway for glacial melt waters, long since abandoned except for a small stream: Southwestern Saskatchewan.

dence of their existence; and, in most cases, they were probably shallow and ephemeral. But silts deposited in the lakes have significantly modified the soils for agricultural purposes. The waters escaping from the lakes also contributed to widening and extending the many southeasterly valleys that were formed as marginal channels and spillways during several glaciations. The largest of these form the coulees of southern Alberta. The melt-water rivers drained east and southeast, leaving channels which typically are 50–200 feet deep (although occasionally they reach 700 feet) and up to half a mile wide. Today they contain either misfit streams or long shallow lakes. In northern Alberta, a series of glacial lakes (Lake Bycroft, Lake Fahler), which at maximum (Lake Peace) were perhaps bigger than the total area of the southern lakes, occupied the Peace and lower Athabasca valleys.

The Saskatchewan proglacial lakes formed as the ice sheet withdrew from Alberta. In general, they were larger and fewer than the southern Alberta lakes. They have been named after the cities now established on the lake floors. In the southwest of the province was Lake Swift Current. As the ice front retreated to the northeast, other lakes were formed—among them Lake Rosetown (in which sediments up to 300 feet thick were deposited) and a series of lakes along the south branch of the Saskatchewan River, including Lake Saskatoon. They drained either southeast or east, the latter drainage in particular forming the deep Blackstrap Coulee south of Saskatoon.

Some of the melt waters from the west drained into glacial Lake Regina, which lay between the continental ice (at this time producing Condie moraine, a northwest-southeast ridge a few miles north of the city of Regina) and the high ground of the Missouri Coteau south and southwest of Moose Jaw. The clays deposited in Lake Regina are in many places up to 40 feet deep. Today the bed of the lake is flat to gently undulating. The one-time shores are marked by faint sand beaches and occasionally a wave-cut cliff. At first, Lake Regina drained past Weyburn along the Souris Valley, which had been established in preglacial times and which was deeply entrenched by the melt waters. The greatly enlarged Souris River in turn drained into glacial Lake Souris, which was already in existence in North Dakota and which at the time was draining southwards along the Sheyenne River, eventually reaching the Mississippi.

There followed an overall ice retreat in southern Saskatchewan and Manitoba. Glacial Lake Regina expanded to the north; and when the Qu'Appelle Valley was uncovered, the lake abandoned the Souris spillway and drained through the Qu'Appelle Valley to the Assiniboine and so to Lake Souris and its successor, building a large sand delta south of Virden. The retreat of the ice in turn uncovered northern outlets for Lake Souris, and shortly afterwards it drained through the Pembina trench to yet another lake dammed by ice—Lake Agassiz.

The Pembina trench is one of the most spectacular scenic features of the Prairies. It was formed while the Assiniboine Valley through the Manitoba Escarpment was still blocked by ice. The flat-bottomed trench is over 200 feet deep and 100 miles long, and is cut in bedrock. Even allowing for the probability that the lower section may be a preglacial valley, it is unlikely that the trench was formed wholly at the close of the last glaciation. More likely, it results from the action of melt waters during several glaciations.

The name of Louis Agassiz is commemorated by attachment to the greatest of all the glacial lakes, Lake Agassiz. At its maximum extent, it occupied practically all southern Manitoba and at several places reached 250 miles into northwestern Ontario. The rich clays and silts deposited in it form the best farming land in the Prairies, the Red River Valley of Minnesota, North Dakota, and Manitoba; and together they cover roughly 180,000 square miles, although the lake never occupied the whole of this area at one time. Today lakes Winnipeg, Winnipegosis, Mani-

Herman

Campbell

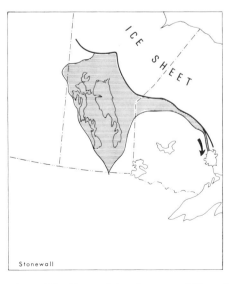

Stonewall

toba, and Dauphin are reminders of its vast-
ness.

Lake Agassiz was formed by the damming
of glacial melt waters between the ice margin
of the continental ice sheet originating to the
northeast and the Manitoba Escarpment. The
first Lake Agassiz in late Wisconsin time
(about 13,000 years ago) was trapped in the
Red River Valley in North Dakota (Figs. 4-1
and 4-2). As the ice margin retreated, the
lake extended north along the east side of the
Manitoba Escarpment. The waters drained
southwards to the Mississippi through the
Lake Traverse outlet and by the Minnesota
River. As the spillway was lowered by erosion,
the lake level was stable and a conspicuous
beach, the Campbell beach, was formed at a
height of 1,040 feet on the international
border. Farther north, west of Dauphin, subsequent warping of the crust has raised the
Campbell beach nearly 100 feet above the
southern end. The strand lines of this phase
are often very conspicuous, consisting of
gravel bars, shingle beaches, and wave-cut
bluffs which are so distinct that the local
farmers often correctly recognize their origin.
Arden, Manitoba, is built directly on this
beach, and one of the town's oldest houses is
called, appropriately enough, Agassiz House.
During this phase, the rivers entering the lake
from the west were building deltas, the largest
of which was constructed by the Assiniboine
and extends east from Brandon to beyond the
military training area around Shilo, where the
sand dunes are particularly prominent.

Retreat of the ice now uncovered outlets
in northwestern Ontario, and the lake fell
and possibly disappeared. This period has
been dated at about 11,000 years ago. The
ice advanced once again and, although it
failed to occupy southern Manitoba completely, the level of Lake Agassiz rose at first

Fig. 4-1   Lake Agassiz: three phases in the
history of the glacial lake (modified after Elson)

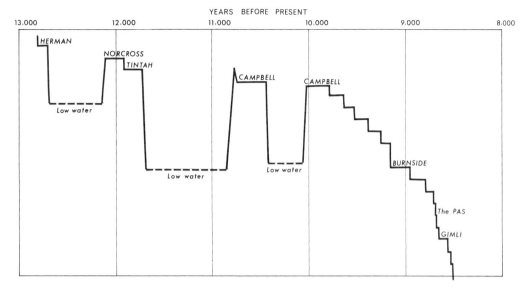

YEARS BEFORE PRESENT

13.000   12.000   11.000   10.000   9.000   8.000

HERMAN

NORCROSS
TINTAH

Low water

CAMPBELL

CAMPBELL

Low water

Low water

BURNSIDE

The PAS

GIMLI

Fig. 4-2   Sequence of water levels of glacial Lake Agassiz (after Elson)

to about the level of the Campbell beach. Subsequently, the level began to fall; and finally, after several fluctuations, Lake Agassiz drained to Hudson Bay as the ice barrier to the north disappeared about 8,000 B.P.

The preceding pages have outlined the proglacial lake sequence in the southern Prairies, and the significance of these lakes in creating the present landscape has been described. No attempt will be made to show the situation farther north; but over large areas, it was similar. In the Mackenzie Lowlands, both Great Slave and Great Bear lakes were at one time more extensive and were joined along the edge of the Shield. On the Canadian Shield west of Hudson Bay, the rivers drain eastwards; and as in the Prairies, they were blocked by the Laurentide ice sheet with the creation of large glacial lakes, particularly in the basin of the Thelon River.

Lakes of the Clay Belt of Northern Ontario and Western Quebec

Just as lakes Winnipeg, Manitoba, and Winnipegosis have a distinguished parentage, Lake Abitibi, in the northern mining districts of Quebec and Ontario, can claim a more illustrious past. The region along and south

of the northern Canadian National transcontinental railway line via Senneterre, Kapuskasing, and Hearst is thickly plastered with clays, usually varved. By now, the reader will recognize such deposits as the characteristic mark of ice-margin lakes.

As the Laurentide ice front receded northwards over the height of land in northern Ontario and western Quebec and began its long retreat down the Hudson Bay slope, ponded waters appeared just as they had done thousands of years previously—in the Erie and Michigan basins. At first, there were two distinct glacial lakes. Lake Barlow was confined to the deep trench that now contains Lake Timiskaming (Lake Barlow's postglacial descendent). Farther west, in the area that is now the headstream zone of the many rivers flowing into the western shore of James Bay, Lake Ojibway came into being (the name and the facts were both provided by A. P. Coleman). These lakes had only a brief separate existence. The ice withdrew to a position along or north of the CN transcontinental railway, and two lakes merged as Lake Barlow–Ojibway, which extended from the Waswanipi Basin of Quebec almost as far as Lake Nipigon in Ontario, a distance of 600 miles. The old beaches have been little mapped, for they lie deeply within thick forest. But the thick clays spread by the lake contribute to the Clay Belt, which has been one of Canada's most recent pioneer frontiers, in both Quebec and Ontario. The bare granite-gneiss of the Shield rarely provides enough soil for agriculture; but the clays give a continuous, though difficult, soil.

For a short time, part of the waters of Lake Barlow–Ojibway drained through Lake Nipigon, but the major outlet was by the Timiskaming trench to the Ottawa. North of Mattawa, the modern Ottawa River follows the spillway, just as the Mattawa River marks the course of the torrent that drained the Nipissing Great Lakes at a somewhat later date. Lake Barlow–Ojibway drained as the ice to the north finally disintegrated, probably about 7,500–8,000 years ago. Shortly before this, one final surge of the ice margin carried it about 70 miles forwards, a phase that is known as the Cochrane advance. Within a few centuries, however, the Wisconsin icecap had melted.

The Great Lakes

The most conspicuous effect of the Pleistocene glaciations on the scenery of North America was the creation of the Great Lakes. Unmatched by any other group of glacial lakes in the world, they have attracted the detailed attention of scientists in the United States and Canada. Pride of place goes to Frank B. Taylor, of the U.S. Geological Survey, who worked in conjunction with Frank Leverett, a great pioneer of Pleistocene geology. In 1915, these researchers published a report called *The Pleistocene of Indiana and Michigan and the History of the Great Lakes*, which summed up many years of research and which is among the finest physiographic studies ever written. Six years earlier, Fairchild had published another masterly study on the northern slopes of the New York Appalachians (the district bounded by Buffalo, Syracuse, and Utica). In Canada, the origins of Lake Ontario were analyzed in similar style by A. P. Coleman. Other men

who contributed greatly were W. A. Johnston, J. W. Goldthwait, J. W. Spencer (in some ways the real pioneer), and W. C. Alden.

Since 1915, detailed studies have contributed new stages and minor corrections to the work of Taylor and Leverett. With the development of radiocarbon dating, it was expected that an absolute time scale could be added to the relative scale already in being; but many unsolved problems remain. Indeed, further research often seems to produce more questions than it resolves. Although there have been considerable advances since 1915, probably at the time of writing less is known with certainty than was thought to have been determined once and for all half a century ago.

The first major problem, and one by no means solved, is how the lake basins were formed. A diastrophic origin must be excluded, and they appear to result from geomorphic processes. The most likely is that the basins were originally broad lowlands developed by rivers on the relatively weaker sedimentary rocks lying between the Canadian Shield and the Appalachians. The course of this hypothetical system is controversial, but ultimately it may have joined the headwaters of the Mississippi. The alternative, that the rivers flowed to the St. Lawrence, is less probable because of the apparent youth of the middle St. Lawrence. When the early ice sheets swept over the Great Lakes region, erosion by the ice was concentrated in the lowlands, which were deepened relative to the more resistant adjacent areas. As the ice retreated, the outlets from the lowlands across the somewhat higher ground were partly blocked by till and moraines and so the Great Lakes came into being—not with one glaciation, but after repeated glaciations, and almost certainly more restricted advances and retreats during interstadials in single glaciations. How much deepening is due to rivers and how much to ice remains uncertain, although in total it was very considerable; the eastern end of Lake Superior, for example, is crossed by submarine valleys that at one point are more than 700 feet *below* sea level.

Early Lake Stages

The story of the late Wisconsin Great Lakes begins with the thawing and retreat of the continental ice. The glacier front became lobate, and distinct lobes occupied basins now filled by Green Bay, Lake Michigan, Saginaw Bay, and Lake Erie. As these lobes retreated, probably more than 14,500 years ago, the first basins to emerge from the ice were at the south end of Lake Michigan, which was occupied by a body of water named Lake Chicago, and southwest Lake Erie, which has been called Lake Maumee (Fig. 4-3). The surface of the latter was over 200 feet higher than the present lake. At first, Lake Chicago drained through the site of modern Chicago into the Des Plaines River, and thence by the Illinois River to the Mississippi. This channel, long ago abandoned by the lakes themselves, has been reopened by man, for it carries the Chicago Canal and the 9-foot navigation channel of the Chicago-to-the-Gulf Waterway. Lake Maumee at first drained to the Wabash River, but a series of oscillations followed in which the levels of the lakes varied. Lake Chicago may have vanished temporarily and Lake Maumee, abandoning its Wabash outlet, escaped across Michigan to Lake Chicago. Further retreat left a lake in the Saginaw Basin.

The Port Huron (Mankato) Substage

The climate once more deteriorated, and the ice thrust forwards to form the moraines of the Port Huron system about 13,200 years ago. The readvance of the ice again separated the Saginaw and Erie basins. In the latter, Lake Whittlesey was created, with a shoreline at 730 feet above present sea level. The lake drained by a new spillway at Ubly across the thumb of Michigan to a re-creation of the Saginaw water-body, called Lake Saginaw II. Thence the drainage went via the Grand River Valley to Lake Chicago, and ultimately to the Mississippi through the Chicago spillway.

Several new spillways make their appearance about this time, although some had been functioning at earlier dates. The Superior Basin was still ice covered, but its melt waters were flooding to the Mississippi via the St. Croix River. The Green Bay lobe had created minor lakes in central Wisconsin, draining to the Mississippi via the Wisconsin and Rock rivers. Finally, in northern New York a complex lake, occupying the deep valleys of the Finger Lake District, spilled past Elmira to the Susquehanna.

Ice-free and lake-free land in southwestern Ontario was now quite extensive. The Port Huron moraine system in Ontario is part of the Horseshoe moraines that ring the central part of the peninsula. It runs from Wyoming near the south end of Lake Huron to points near Lucknow, Singhampton, and Brantford. Backed by the Huron, Georgian Bay, and Ontario ice lobes, the moraine-girt landscape was washed by Lake Whittlesey on the south where well-developed beaches mark the old shoreline. Melt-water torrents discharged into the lake, the finest flowing from near Caledon to Brantford, where it deposited in the lake an immense sand and gravel delta.

The harsh arctic climate froze the surface of Lake Whittlesey deeply each winter. During the brief summer, the disintegrating lake ice bore down upon the shores and pushed up the beach gravels into ice-shove ridges. The stormy climate, with its attendant waves, may further have accentuated this ridging. However this may be, the Whittlesey beach often stands several feet above the surrounding plain, and blocks valleys 25 feet deep like a railway embankment, not unlike Burlington bar in modern Lake Ontario.

During the next thousand years, the oscillating ice front lay across southwestern Ontario. As the glacier moved backwards and forwards, there were variations in lake level, shorelines, and outlets. The lakes in the Lake Erie and southern Lake Huron basins have been called Wayne, Warren, Grassmere, and Lundy. They were followed by a marked retreat of the ice which about 12,500 years ago uncovered western Lake Superior and the greater part of the other lakes. The ice front at the time lay from Georgian Bay to the

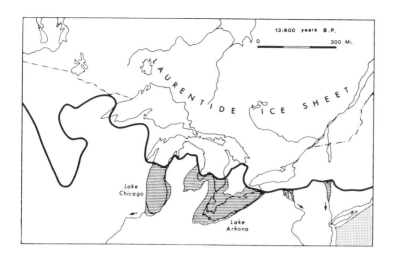

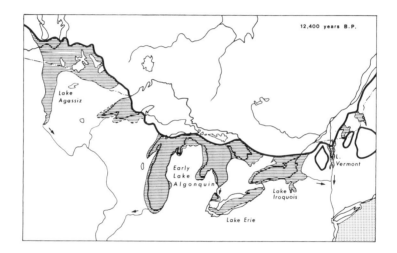

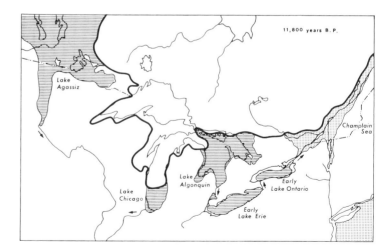

Fig. 4-3   The evolution of
the Great Lakes (I) (after
Geological Survey of Canada)

TABLE 4-1
LATE GLACIAL AND POSTGLACIAL
EVENTS IN SOUTHERN ONTARIO
AND QUEBEC

No. of years ago	Southern Ontario	Quebec
1,000		
2,000		
3,000		
4,000		
5,000	North Bay outlet of upper Great Lakes abandoned	Last remnants of ice sheet in northern Quebec
6,000		
7,000		
8,000	Early Nipissing Great Lakes	Lake in St. Lawrence Lowlands; Champlain Sea ends
9,000	Low-level stage in	
10,000	Huron Basin	
11,000	North Bay outlet uncovered	
	Valders readvance of ice (Northwestern Ontario)	St. Narcisse moraine
12,000	Early Lake Algonquin Lake Iroquois	Champlain Sea forms Covey Hill channel
13,000	Port Huron (Mankato) ice advance	First land uncovered in Eastern Townships
14,000		
	Southwest corner of Erie Basin uncovered from ice	
15,000		

Thousand Islands. In the Ontario Basin was a body of water, Lake Iroquois, which was about 100 feet higher than modern Lake Ontario.

Lake Iroquois received waters from Lake Erie through the Niagara River and from a line of spillways from Georgian Bay that today are occupied roughly by the Trent River and Canal in south-central Ontario. The latter spillways were abandoned with the disappearance of the ice sheet, but the former has continued to contain the Niagara River to the present day.

The magnificent falls of Niagara, the only survivor of several great spillway-cataracts, mark the point at which most of the descent of the Niagara cuesta is achieved. In the course of the century, this fall has receded towards Lake Erie by erosion of its lip. It is still receding at about 3.8 feet per annum (about a mile in 1,400 years) and at this rate will begin to drain Lake Erie in 25,000 to 30,000 years. For many years, geologists tried to compute the age of the falls in this way. The gorge below the falls is 6½ miles long, and it was formerly thought that 20,000 to 35,000 years would have been needed to cut it. It has been discovered, however, that in fact the Whirlpool Rapids gorge has a thick fill of glacial drift, and that a buried gorge (the St. David's Channel) runs from the Whirlpool to the cuesta's face (Fig. 4-4). In other words, a Niagara gorge and falls existed *before* the Wisconsin glaciation, and much of the postglacial activity has been the removal of till rather than the creation of a new gorge.

Lake Iroquois drained along Mohawk Valley, although for a brief period it may have drained around the north edge of the Adirondacks into the Lake Champlain Basin. While Lake Iroquois was in being, the shores were being tilted, sinking progressively beneath the lake in the southwest and rising in the east. From the Niagara River to Hamilton, To-

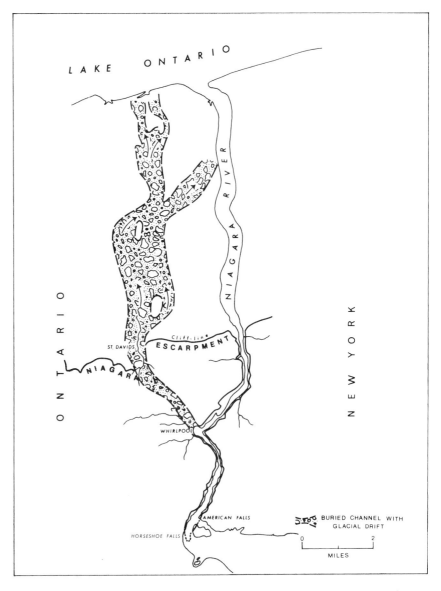

Fig. 4-4   The present and former Niagara gorge (after Hobson and Terasmae)

ronto, and eastwards as far as the Bay of Quinte, the lake left conspicuous elevated shorelines. At many points, the Iroquois bluff is a striking feature. It swings across the City of Toronto, forming a particularly fine cliff, its position marked by Davenport Avenue. At Hamilton, the most striking evidence of the work of Lake Iroquois is the celebrated Hamilton bar, built up by storm waves across the head of the basin; the bar is 2 miles long and 116 feet above present lake level, and has long been used as a natural causeway for road and rail. It is very similar in origin to the modern Burlington bar. South of the lake, the United States cities of Utica and Rochester are built on the beaches of the former lake, and Rome guards the outlet channels.

For most of the life of Lake Iroquois, the Straits of Mackinac, the northern channel that joins lakes Huron and Michigan, were depressed by the weight of the ice and one lake—Lake Algonquin—occupied the two basins. There were broadly three principal stages before the ice readvanced for the final time, shown in the table below.

Following these stages, the ice made one further surge forwards—the Valders advance, about 11,800 years ago. Although there is still some uncertainty about the exact position of the ice, it appears to have advanced no farther than a line from north of Ottawa through central Ontario to the Soo. All of the Superior Basin and a large part of the Michigan Basin were reoccupied by the glacier.

With the final retreat of the ice, Lake Algonquin reformed. Although the ice sheet was no longer an important barrier, the shores of the lakes were not identical with contemporary beaches, because the earth's crust had not fully recovered from the depression produced by the ice. Lakes Erie and Ontario quickly became much as they are today (Fig. 4-5). Above Lake St. Clair, however, a fairly prolonged low-level lake stage followed, particularly in the Huron and Michigan basins, during which they were drained to the Ottawa through the French River–Lake Nipissing–Mattawa River Valley (usually called the North Bay outlet). The St. Clair and Chicago outlets were dry. Continued uplift in the northern parts of the basins led to the expansion of the upper lakes to create the Lake Nipissing stage about 8,500 years ago. The North Bay outlet continued to be used until between 7,000–6,000 B.P., when a two-outlet (and for a time three-outlet) phase began, much water continuing east along the Ottawa and the rest draining southwards into Lake Erie past Chicago. The latter outlet was abandoned, however, when the Port Huron channel had been eroded 3 or 4 feet.

The main Nipissing beach was cut at 605 feet (24 feet above the present lake level) south of the Algonquin hinge (a line from the head of the lakes, to Green Bay and Goderich, Ontario), but rises northwards to about 700 feet on the north shore of Lake Superior and at North Bay. The beach strands

Lake	Outlet and Correlatives
Early Algonquin (about 12,500 years B.P.)	St. Clair River over Port Huron moraine to Lake St. Clair (newly created), thence to Lake Erie (also newly created). Lake Algonquin was confined to the Huron Basin and by a northern link to Lake Chicago.
Algonquin (Kirkfield phase) (about 12,400 years B.P.)	Trent River and Kawartha Lakes past Kirkfield, Ontario, and Fenelon Falls, into Lake Iroquois. St. Clair River dry.
Algonquin (main phase) Multiple outlets (about 12,200–11,500 years B.P.)	Three outlets: Kirkfield, Chicago, and St. Clair River. Some southward tilt, tending to throw main drainage through St. Clair and Chicago, and to dry up Kirkfield.

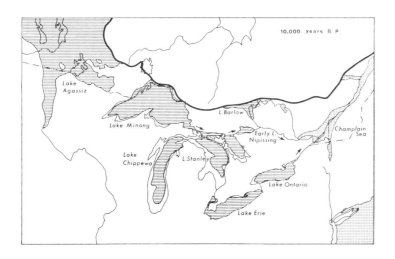

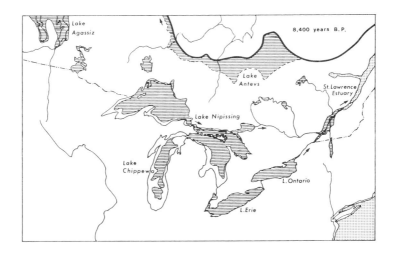

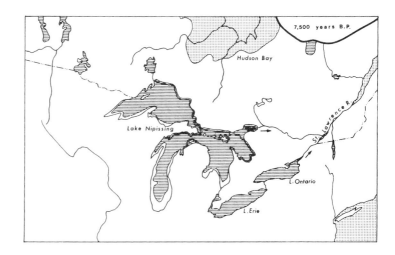

Fig. 4-5 The evolution of
the Great Lakes (II) (after
Geological Survey of Canada)

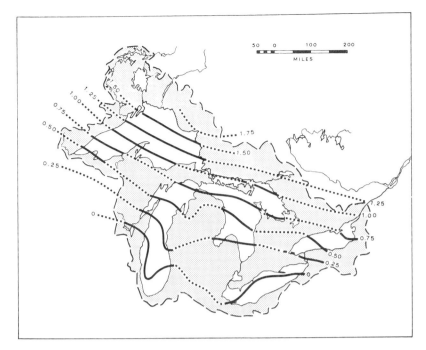

Fig. 4-6   Relative crustal movements in the Great Lakes drainage basin, in feet per century (after Clark and Persoage)

diverge, showing that some of this uplift took place during the life of the lake.

The end of Lake Nipissing came with renewed uplift to the north, still along the Algonquin hinge. This uplift raised the North Bay outlet above water level, and the whole flow was diverted to the St. Clair–Erie–Niagara outlet to Lake Ontario and the St. Lawrence, slightly raising the level of Lake Erie. At the same time, the narrow strait linking Lake Superior was raised above the level of waters in the Michigan–Huron basins, so that Lake Superior was separated from the remaining lakes. Its waters spill to Lake Huron through the St. Mary's River, a winding 60-mile spillway with a drop of 21 feet (chiefly at Sault Ste. Marie).

The date and duration of the Nipissing Great Lakes remains in some doubt. The final withdrawal of the ice from the North Bay outlet was shortly after the retreat from the Valders advance, probably about 11,200 B.P. Abandonment of the North Bay outlet and the closing stages of the Lake Nipissing phase can be dated about 5,000 B.P.

The landscape of southern Ontario (and the adjacent American states) has been profoundly modified by the episode described in this section. The deep laminated clays, as well as the coarser sands that usually overlie them and which are found in the vicinity of the lakes in all parts of southern Ontario, are lacustrine deposits. In addition, there are striking erosional forms produced by the waves, including the Iroquois bluff near Lake Ontario and the Algonquin and Nipissing bluffs found on the south side of Georgian Bay; and finally, there are the spillways, which today carry undersized streams along channels that once drained huge lakes.

Lakes in Eastern Canada

Glacial lakes in eastern Canada were never extensive. Although the higher relief did not preclude the formation of glacial lakes, it certainly restricted their expansion. The St. Lawrence Lowlands were dominated by the Champlain Sea at the close of the glaciation, but short-lived lakes also occupied the area. The first glacial lake to appear was in the Champlain Valley, where Lake Vermont was dammed against the ice front that was retreating northwards. At first, the waters drained to the Hudson River through a spillway at Coveville, New York. By the time the ice had withdrawn to the latitude of St. Albans and Port Kent, the lake began to receive overflow from the Great Lakes via the Covey Hill outlet on the northern edge of the Adirondacks. A little later, the escaping waters uncovered a lower channel of the Hudson at Schuylerville, New York; the southern part of Lake Vermont drained, but the main body continued to exist at a lower level, being held up by a rock barrier at Fort Ann, New York. These waters ultimately drained across the disintegrating ice dam in the St. Lawrence Valley. For a brief period, a lake may have existed throughout the lowlands before the Champlain Sea broke in.

In the Eastern Townships of Quebec, the retreat of the ice northwards and westwards led to the creation of long narrow lakes that drained southwards to the Connecticut system. Varved clays, boulder pavements, and low bluffs from this stage can be found in many parts of southeastern Quebec close to the Vermont border.

Glacial lakes in the Maritime Provinces were small, mainly because the natural flow of the rivers was towards the Atlantic Ocean away from the ice sheet. The largest lake, named Lake Madawaska, formed in the upper Saint John Valley and its tributary valley of the Madawaska, probably behind a morainic dam at Grand Falls, New Brunswick.

Selected Readings

Hough, J. L., *Geology of the Great Lakes*, Urbana, University of Illinois Press, 1958, 313 pp.

Mayer-Oakes, W. J. (ed.), *Life, Land and Water*, Winnipeg, University of Manitoba Press, 1967, 414 pp.

Prest, V. K., *Quaternary Geology of Canada* in Douglas, R. J. W. (ed.), *Geology and Economic Minerals of Canada*, Ottawa, Queen's Printer, 1971, pp. 676–764.

5

The Changing Sea Level

In the earlier discussion of the geological background, it was at once evident that throughout much of geological time the sea shore has moved backwards and forwards across the land—sometimes transgressing, at other times regressing—and that this movement led, among other things, to the deposition of the sediments that now form many of the rocks of Canada. These shifts of land and sea continued through the Tertiary period into the Pleistocene epoch, when they were more rapid than at any time in the recent geological past.

In many parts of the world normally thought of as stable, late Tertiary transgressions have left marine sediments and wave-planed topography. Some clear evidence of such changes is found in northwestern Canada and adjacent Alaska, where the sands and gravels of the Beaufort Formation were deposited along the shores of a sea that for a time was at least 100–200 feet higher than it is today. Northern Canada also shows unquestionable evidence of low-water stages;

for it is clear that, in the late Tertiary or early Quaternary times, the channels and bays of the Arctic Archipelago, and Hudson Bay, were dry land except for their deepest parts. They were drained by rivers, traces of whose valleys still occur beneath the sea.

During the Pleistocene interglacials, the evidence from many parts of the world is that the sea level was higher than it is today by possibly one or two hundred feet in the early part and some tens of feet in the later periods (Fig. 5-1). Although high Pleistocene sea levels occurred on the Atlantic seaboard of the United States from New Jersey southwards, there is little evidence of them in Canada. Whether this implies that the evidence has been destroyed by the glaciations, or that, unlike other parts of the world, it did not occur, is uncertain. Rock platforms a few feet above present sea level in Nova Scotia may be of this age.

If the interglacial sea levels have left little mark, the reverse is true of late glacial and postglacial changes; these have profoundly

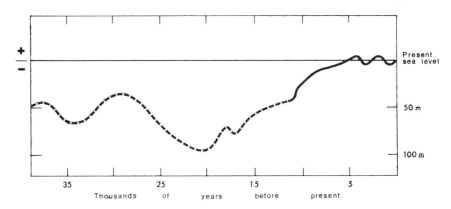

Fig. 5-1   Eustatic changes of sea level. The fluctuating level of the sea is shown for stable tropical areas during the past 37,000 years. The curve is highly speculative in the early part of the period.

Plate 5-1   An elevated delta formed by a tributary stream to the Aston River, Somerset Island, N.W.T., when the land was depressed relative to sea level. Subsequently, as the land emerged from the sea, the stream cut into the delta and formed an alluvial fan below it.

affected the Arctic, the eastern Canadian, and the southwest British Columbia shores. Characteristically, the sea level was highest during the retreat of the ice from an area. The resulting features take different forms in various areas. They include the raised deltas around Chaleur Bay and along the south shore of the St. Lawrence estuary below Rivière-du-Loup; the storm boulder ridges on the hills around the Montreal Plain; and, above all, in the Arctic lowlands, elevated strand lines, cliffs, and marine sediments of spectacular proportions, particularly where the bedrock is limestone. Indeed, it was in the Arctic that these features first attracted the attention of seventeenth-century European explorers; and the Eskimos before them had a long folk tradition to account for beaches and marine shells located several hundred feet above the present sea.

Recent elevated marine features are not unique to Canada, but are found in almost all parts of the world that have been glaciated. About a century ago, Jamieson in Scotland and Shaler independently in the United States described the mechanism by which they were produced. It is now known that the major Pleistocene continental ice sheets were at least 2 miles and possibly nearly 4 miles thick in the centre. The Laurentide ice sheet over eastern North America at its maximum may have contained more than 3 million cubic miles of ice. The ice for this and the other continental glaciers ultimately must have originated from snowfall from the seas, and so much water was withdrawn from them that there was a world-wide fall of sea level of more than 300 feet. This drop uncovered almost all the continental shelves, now submerged by the sea. When the ice sheets melted, the sea level rose again (Fig. 5-2). About 10,000 years ago—by which time most Canadian coastal areas, except in the Arctic, were free of ice—the sea level was

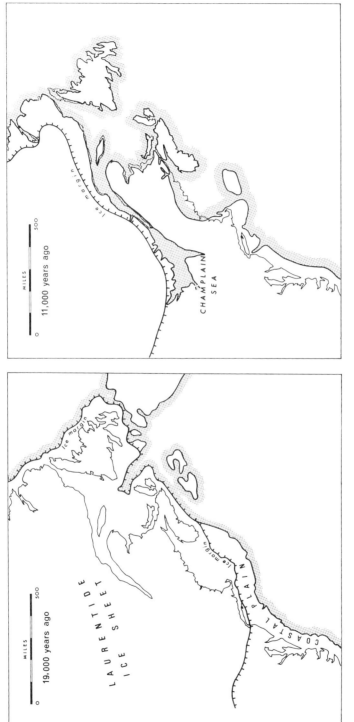

Fig. 5-2   The eastern seaboard of Canada and the United States in the Late Quaternary. About 19,000 years ago, when the Wisconsin ice was near its maximum, there were large islands off the Atlantic Provinces and the continental shelf was exposed off the United States. About 8,000 years later (11,000 years ago), the ice front lay over Quebec and Labrador; in the south, the coast still lay on the shelf, but farther north the sea was in a transgressive phase, or approximated today's position.

TABLE 5-1

POSTGLACIAL CHANGES OF SEA LEVEL RELATIVE TO LAND BURIED BENEATH PLEISTOCENE ICE SHEETS

Date of ice withdrawal	Position relative to maximum ice sheet	Subsequent shore movement	Land changes today	Type locality	Change of sea level relative to land
Early (> 12,500 years ago)	Marginal	Transgression	Stable	N. Yukon coast	
	Central	Not applicable		—	—
Middle period (9,000–10,000 years ago)	Marginal	Regression followed by transgression	Stable	Labrador coast	
	Central	Regression	Stable or gently rising	Coronation Gulf	
Late (6,000–7,000 years ago)	Marginal	Not applicable		—	—
	Central	Regression	Rising	Hudson Bay	

Plate 5-2   The highest level reached by the postglacial sea on the shores of Wager Bay. The line on the hillside, marking the lower limit of drift and the highest sea level, is now 385 feet above the sea.

about 100 feet lower than it is today. In the next 4,000 years, it rose by this amount; and from then to the present, although there have been oscillations of up to about 10 feet, there has been no major change in either direction. These oscillations seem to have resulted from climatic change—indeed, a consistent rise in the last few decades of about 1 inch in 20 years has been observed.

The influence on Canadian scenery of the low sea levels at the height of the glaciation was slight, since ice lay over the continental shelf. The crust was affected directly by the weight of the ice, however, and was depressed by about one-third of the thickness of the ice. Of course, by the time the ice melted, the crust had risen a great deal from its maximum depression; but it is not perfectly elastic, and so there was a lag. When the ice vanished from an area, the land was still lower than in preglacial times, and the sea invaded the coastal areas. The extent of the transgression depended on when and how quickly deglaciation occurred and how thick the ice had been (Table 5-1).

The amount of rebound since the disappearance of the ice sheet increases roughly from the extreme margins of the Pleistocene icecap towards its centre. In Canada, emerged features are no higher than a few feet in the northwest and on the Atlantic shore of Nova Scotia, but they exceed 900 feet at localities on the east side of Hudson Bay. In general, along the Atlantic seaboard from Cape Breton northwards, emergence has been from 200–300 feet; around Hudson Bay and in the southern archipelago, it is 400–700 feet; and in the northern islands, it is generally less than 300 feet. The most rapid emergence occurred immediately after the ice withdrew, and a rate of uplift of 30–40 feet per century appears to have been common for short periods.

Around the outer perimeter of the ice sheet, emergence was so rapid as the ice withdrew that, when the crust had returned to its preglacial position, the sea level was still lower than it is at present. The result was that the shore was displaced out onto the continental shelf. This happened around the Bay of Fundy, where the present marshlands were undoubtedly dry land, and almost certainly around Prince Edward Island, on the Atlantic coast of Nova Scotia and in southeast Newfoundland. As the sea rose again, the low-lying lands were drowned and the submerged forests that are found below high tide on many Maritime beaches were formed. It must be noted, however, that along the Atlantic coast regional crustal movements that have nothing to do with the glaciations also were occurring. Consequently, on the Maritime coasts we have evidence of both emergence in elevated beaches and deltas including the prominent features on Cape Breton Island

and around Chaleur Bay (Fig. 5-3), and submergence in long estuaries, the drowned valleys of the postglacial rivers.

It is probable that similar events occurred along the shore of the Beaufort Sea from Banks Island and the Mackenzie Delta to the Alaska border, but less is known about this area.

The emergence of the crust was continuous, although diminishing. In some parts, the world-wide rise of sea level temporarily kept pace with the crustal rebound, and then there was a period of stationary sea level before emergence began again. This phenomenon was first observed in Scandinavia, where it produced very marked wide beaches formed by continued emergence. In Canada, such conspicuous pauses in the uplift of the land have been found on Cape Breton Island, on the Labrador coast, and in eastern Baffin

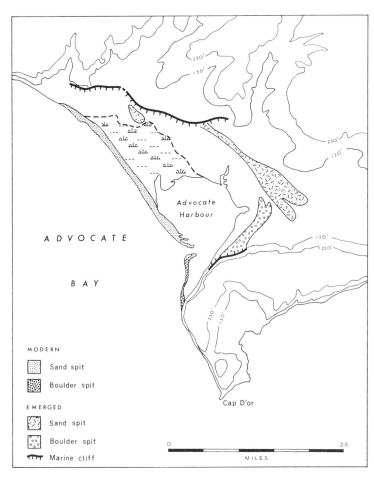

Fig. 5-3   Cap d'Or and Advocate Bay. In early postglacial time, the Cap d'Or hills of Nova Scotia were an island separated from the mainland by a strait more than a mile wide. The west end of the strait was closed by two spits now elevated to about 50 feet. After the land had emerged, a new spit system developed, shutting off Advocate Harbour from the sea. (After Bjorns.)

Island; but in most places, the land appears to have risen more or less continuously (Fig. 5-4).

The effect of the transgression is often spectacular, but it varies considerably according to local conditions. In the plains on the south side of Queen Maud and Coronation gulfs, silts were widely distributed, blanketing the low rock knobs that are typical of the Canadian Shield in this area. Conditions were somewhat similar in the St. Lawrence Lowlands; in the deep estuary between the Laurentian escarpment and the Canadian Appalachians, the waters of the Champlain Sea received from the surrounding land quantities of silt and clay that were deposited in the lowest part of the lowlands and today underlie many areas. At the same time, rivers from the melting ice were forming deltas on the plain. Only later, as the sea fell, did the sands spread over the lowlands to mantle the

clays. Later still, the sands were partly removed by the rivers after the sea had withdrawn.

In other areas, constructional forms are more conspicuous—notably the shingle ridges that are particularly prominent on the limestone of the Hudson Bay Lowland, on the Foxe Basin Lowlands, and on Anticosti Island. In the flattest of these areas, the transgression has formed an entirely new landscape with the dry, often barren shingle ridges separating ill-drained zones with lagoons, marsh vegetation, and peat.

We have seen already that everywhere the land was rising quickly at the beginning of the transgression. Uplift of a foot every two or three years has been estimated for the areas where submergence was greatest. Within 3,000–4,000 years, however, the rate of uplift had fallen off rapidly; and in most areas the sea had retreated to roughly its present

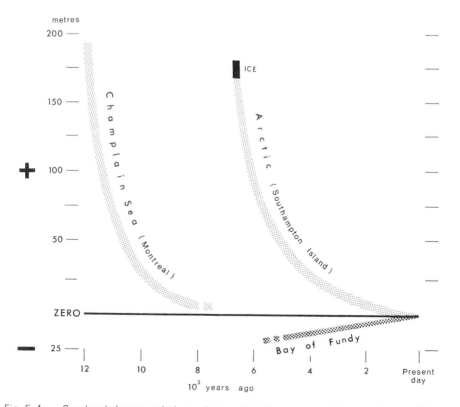

Fig. 5-4   Sea-level changes relative to the land that have occurred in several parts of Canada in the last 12,000 years

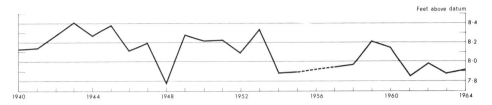

Feet above datum

Fig. 5-5   Emergence of the land as shown by the fall of sea level during the summer months, 1940–1964, at Churchill, Manitoba

position. There is a residual amount of uplift still outstanding—possibly several hundred feet around Hudson Bay—and emergence is continuing. At Churchill, where there has been a tide gauge since 1929, the present emergence is about 1.3 feet a century (Fig. 5-5). This figure is surprisingly low; for it has been known for a long time from tide gauges and the emergence of historical marks that in the northern Baltic, in an area that was near the centre of the Scandinavian ice sheet, elevation is about 3 feet a century.

Delayed crustal changes related to the weight of the ice sheet may also occur in the interior of the continent, but they are less easy to recognize. It seems, however, that the land around the Great Lakes is being tilted today, as the Canadian coasts rise relative to the American.

Selected Readings

Andrews, J. T., *A Geomorphological Study of Post-Glacial Uplift with Particular Reference to Northern Canada*, London, Institute of British Geographers, 1970, 156 pp.

Curray, J. R., *Late Quaternary History, Continental Shelves of the United States* in Wright, H. E., Jr., and D. C. Frey (eds.), *The Quaternary of the United States*, Princeton, N.J., Princeton University Press, 1965, pp. 723–735.

Elson, J. A., "Late Quaternary Marine Submergence of Quebec", *Rev. Géogr. Montréal*, Vol. 23, 1969, pp. 247–258.

Fairbridge, R. W., *Eustatic Changes in Sea Level in Physics and Chemistry of the Earth*, Vol. 4, New York, Pergamon Press, 1961, pp. 99–185.

Flint, R. F., *Glacial and Quaternary Geology*, New York, Wiley, 1971, Ch. 12 and 13, pp. 315–366.

Grant, D. R., "Recent Coastal Submergence of the Maritime Provinces, Canada", *Can. Jour. Earth Sciences*, Vol. 7, 1970, pp. 676–689.

Karrow, P. F., *The Champlain Sea and its Sediments* in Leggett, R. F., *Soils in Canada*, Toronto, University of Toronto Press, 1961, pp. 97–108.

6

The Physiographic Regions of Canada

It is evident to everybody who travels across Canada that there are strong regional differences between landscapes in various parts of the country. Terms such as the Maritimes, the Prairies, or the West Coast (particularly when the last term is used synonymously with the Cordillera) are far more than political expressions and usually conjure up impressions of the scenery, climate, and the life of the people in these areas. By the end of the eighteenth century, European explorers had shown that the northern half of the continent was divided readily into major geographical blocks; and long before Confederation, the major environmental and future political divisions of the southern part of the country were recognized.

The largest global landscape or physiographic units are usually considered to be the continents. The next class, physiographic divisions or regions, are subcontinental in size and are several hundred thousand square miles in extent. Only the broadest generalizations apply throughout each division. Further hierarchical subdivision may be made, until ultimately the smallest unit is an isolated landform.

The development of the regional concept in geomorphology originated in the United States. The same landscape differences that had been recognized by the traders of the Hudson's Bay Company and the Northwest Company as they pushed westwards and northwestwards across Canada were evident to the explorers and surveyors of the mid-nineteenth century in the United States. The major United States physiographic regions were first recognized by scientist-explorers. In seeking rational criteria for defining the regions, they recognized the role that rocks and particularly rock structure played in landform

development. Therefore this became the major criterion, and in the largest units the only criterion, for physiographic regionalization. Early views were consolidated in the works of Powell (1896) and were expanded in the next two decades, culminating in a map prepared by Fenneman for the Association of American Geographers in 1916 that was widely accepted and has been the basis of most subsequent physiographic subdivisions of the United States.

In Canada, the comparable stage was reached much later and in a somewhat different manner: the northern part of the country remained largely unknown; and in the first half of the twentieth century, it rarely entered into general discussions. The southern half was often thought of as a physiographic appendage or continuation of the United States, and extension of the United States boundaries was the normal response of geographical textbook writers in both countries. Any such projection assumes that the dominant structural influences found in the landscapes of the United States are equally dominant in Canada.

A special Canadian viewpoint was not presented until 1964, when Bostock argued that the initial physiographic subdivision of the North American continent should be into two regions, the Canadian Shield and the remainder of the continent (or the Borderlands). In the present work, a three-fold division into the Canadian Shield, the border plains, and the extensive mountain belts, with a fourth small Arctic coastal plain, is considered more appropriate for descriptive purposes. Fig. 6-1 shows the principal physiographic regions of Canada.

A satisfactory subdivision of the Shield into

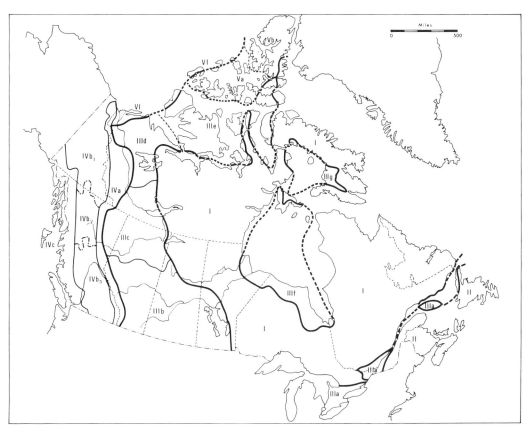

A	I	The Canadian Shield	IV	The Western Cordillera
				a) Eastern mountains
B		The Border Regions		b) Interior plateaus
	II	The Appalachian-Acadian Uplands		and mountains
				c) Coast ranges
	III	The Interior Plains	V	Innuitian Region
		a) St. Lawrence		a) Southern plains and hills
		b) Prairie		b) Northern mountains
		c) Peace-Slave Lowland	VI	Arctic Coastal Plain
		d) Mackenzie		
		e) Arctic		
		f) Hudson Bay		
		g) Foxe Basin		

Fig. 6-1   The principal physiographic regions of Canada

individual units of the magnitude of roughly a quarter million square miles or more is not available. Bostock proposed eight provinces based entirely on geological history, but the relevance to present-day morphology of units that are based on structures formed one to two and one-half billion (10^9) years ago is doubtful.

The second major physiographic unit developed on the flat-lying sedimentary rocks that border the Shield from Anticosti Island and the St. Lawrence plains of southern Quebec, through southern Ontario and the Midwest of the United States, to the Prairies, and eventually northwards to Parry Channel and the southern fringe of the Queen Elizabeth Islands. Throughout this area, plains and low plateaus which have developed on the sedimentary rocks and are often buried under glacial sediments constitute the predominant element of the physical landscape. Further subdivision of the border plains is easy, except in the Prairies, where an accepted division into two in the United States (Central Lowlands and Great Plains) has not been reconciled with a more common Canadian three-fold classification into Manitoba Lowlands, Saskatchewan Plains, and Alberta Plains.

Closely related to the border lowlands are the interior lowlands within the Shield around Hudson Bay, particularly on the south side, and to a lesser extent around Foxe Basin. They have developed on Paleozoic sedimentary rocks that were once far more extensive. In the remote geological past, the interior and exterior plains were probably joined by limestone rocks that covered the Shield.

The third group of regions is those in the Borderlands where the rocks have undergone

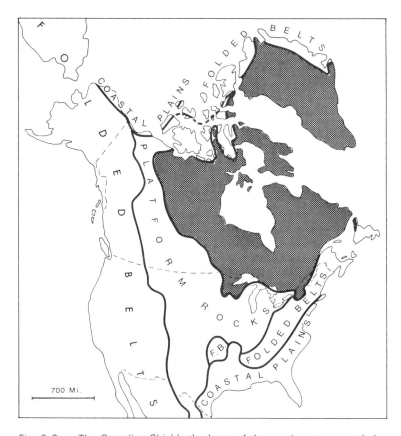

Fig. 6-2   The Canadian Shield: the heart of the continent, surrounded by platform rocks (buried Shield), folded belts, and coastal plains

intensive folding in the past. The most conspicuous and largest of these is the Western Cordillera, embracing almost all British Columbia and the Yukon. The second in rank is in the east and only a small part is in Canada —the folded Appalachian–Acadian region of the Eastern Townships of Quebec, the Maritime Provinces, and Newfoundland. The third folded belt in the far north, known as the Innuitian Province, includes much of the Queen Elizabeth Islands where there is considerable variety among the plateaus and hills of the Parry Islands, the lowlands of the Sverdrup Islands, and the high mountains of Ellesmere and Axel Heiberg islands.

The differences among these three divisions may be summarized as follows. The Shield is dominated by crystalline rocks, generally highly resistant to denudation; here, ancient landscapes survive with only superficial modification, except in a few areas significantly altered by the Pleistocene glaciations. The border plains and plateaus in contrast are geologically young and highly uniform, partly because of the similar response to geomorphic processes over broad areas and to the strong effects of the glaciations. The outer folded belt regions have as their dominant characteristic great variety, which results from intense folding and diverse structural history.

When the continent is examined physiographically as a whole, it is evident that a certain symmetry exists around the Canadian Shield (Fig. 6-2). The only major United States region not mentioned so far, the Gulf Atlantic coastal plain, has as its analogue the Arctic coastal plain of the shores of the Beaufort Sea.

Many of the variations within these regions and between the separate parts have already been indicated in the first part of the book. We shall now proceed to examine the major landforms in the various Canadian physiographic regions.

Selected Readings

Baird, D. M., "Geology and Landforms as Illustrated by Selected Canadian Topographic Maps", *Geol. Surv. Can. Paper* 64-21, 1964, 59 pp.

Bostock, H. S., "A Provisional Physiographic Map of Canada", *Geol. Surv. Can. Paper* 64-35, 1964, 24 pp., and *Geol. Surv. Can. Map*, 1245A, 1970.
Physiographic Subdivisions of Canada in Douglas, R. J. W. (ed.), *Geology and Economic Minerals of Canada*, Ottawa, Queen's Printer, 1971, Ch. 2, pp. 10–30.

Parry, J. T., "Geomorphology in Canada", *Canadian Geographer*, Vol. XI, 1967, pp. 280–311.

Thornbury, W. D., *Regional Geomorphology of the United States*, New York, Wiley, 1965, Ch. 1.

Zaborski, B., *Atlas of Landscapes and Settlements of Eastern Canada*, Montreal, Sir George Williams University, 1972, 200 pp.

7

The Appalachian–Acadian Province

In an early chapter on the geological development of the North American continent, it was described how in Paleozoic times folded mountain ranges formed along the eastern margin of the continent from Alabama to Newfoundland. The worn down remnants of these mountains today comprise the Appalachian–Acadian physiographic province. All Canada southeast of the Appalachian Front, including the Eastern Townships of Quebec and the south side of the St. Lawrence estuary, taking in the Gaspé Peninsula and the Atlantic Provinces, is part of this province. Within this large area, there is a wide variety of scenery. All but a small part of the region is underlain by Paleozoic sediments, but there are great differences in rock type and structure: in some areas, they are highly contorted; in others, they are gently folded; and elsewhere, they are flat-lying. Deep within the crust, igneous rocks were intruded into the roots of the Acadian Mountains as they were

being folded, and volcanoes were active for part of the mountain-building period. Small areas of Precambrian rocks also were incorporated in the mountains, particularly in Newfoundland. Throughout the province, structures are dominated by a southwest-northeast strike that locally becomes north-northeasterly. This strike is reflected in many parts in the orientation of the hill ranges, the rivers and valleys, and the coastline. The rocks have responded to the denudation processes in a variety of ways; and mountains, plateaus, long narrow vales, and broad lowlands are all part of the Acadian scene.

The Eastern Townships

The scenery of the southeast of Quebec, in the area known as the Eastern Townships, between the United States border and the Chaudière River, is a direct continuation of the hills and valleys of northern New Eng-

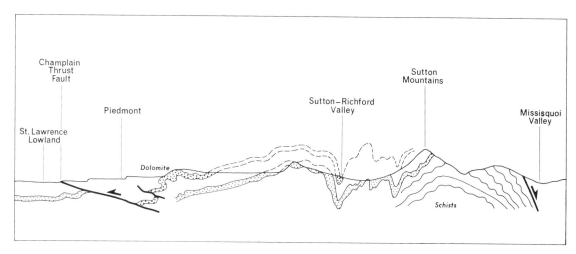

Fig. 7-1   A section through the western margin of the Canadian Appalachians in southern Quebec (after Eakins, Geological Survey of Canada)

land. Between Philipsburg on the east side of Missisquoi Bay (Lake Champlain) and Lévis, opposite Quebec, the western edge of the structural province is formed by a fault, known variously as the Appalachian Front, the Champlain Fault, or Logan's Line (Fig. 7-1). It marks the boundary of the thick sediments that accumulated in the early Paleozoic geosyncline and were thrust northwestwards over the thinner and more stable sediments on the continental shelf underlying what are today the St. Lawrence Lowlands. Logan's Line is rarely associated with a conspicuous surface feature and is often buried by drift. Occasionally, a low, rock bluff some hundreds of yards east of the Line marks the edge of the St. Lawrence Lowlands and the commencement of a gentle rise across the piedmont to the main hill ranges of the Townships.

Although the events of Paleozoic times led to the formation of high mountain ranges, these have long since disappeared in their original form. For a long geological period, the area must have been a lowland with occasional isolated hills. Subsequently, the earth's crust rose by stages; and as the rivers cut valleys in the old surface, new levels were produced which today are often striking features of the landscape. Remnants of the early surface still survive, however, in a few localities. Nowhere are the results of these events more obvious than along the middle Chaudière, where the river and its main tributaries flow in narrow valleys entrenched 400 feet into the main upland. Similar, if smaller, uplands may be found throughout the region.

The major landforms of the Eastern Townships are residual features left as the processes of denudation, mainly fluvial, removed the rocks most susceptible to erosion. In general, rocks that withstand erosion today form the highest areas; but in a few cases, notably the granites, which in the present climate are highly resistant, arc paradoxically part of the lowlands. The main hill-forming rocks are the schists of Cambrian age or older which outcrop in a wide belt to underlie the Sutton Mountains. North of the Montreal–Sherbrooke Autoroute, the zone of schists narrows, and the hills are low or disappear entirely. They reappear as the outcrop widens

Plate 7-1   The Quebec Eastern Townships showing several surfaces of denudation. The main surface extends to the hills, that include the Green Mountains and the Sutton Ranges, in the background. Rivers and lakes are entrenched in valleys 100–300 feet deep in the surface : Stanstead Co., Quebec.

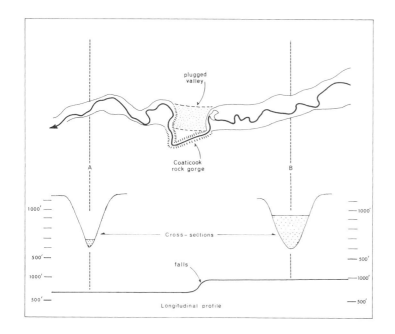

Fig. 7-2 The Coaticook Falls: a characteristic situation in many valleys of the Canadian Appalachians. The valley train and alluvium have been removed by the river from the left side, but are preserved above the rock section of the valley, where the river in early postglacial time flowed off its preglacial valley.

northwest of Asbestos and between Thetford Mines and the Chaudière Valley, where the hills exceed 2,000 feet in several summits. When seen from a distance, the hills appear to have rounded, forest-covered slopes; but on closer examination, the schists are found to have weathered into vertical slabs. The scenery is locally very fine, particularly in the deep passes through the range.

East of the Sutton Mountains, isolated and often conspicuous hills are developed on a belt of intrusive igneous rocks, including the peaks of Mount Orford, Owl Head, Mount Mégantic, and Ham Mountain. In the middle of the Townships, a line of hills of varying height has developed on lavas and quartzites. These hills have the characteristic Appalachian southwest-northeast orientation, beginning with the Bunker Hill escarpment overlooking Fitch Bay and expanding into the Stoke Range. A third line of hills, the Border Range along the New Hampshire and Maine frontier, is the northern end of the White Mountains of New England.

Between the main ranges are flat upland surfaces, often broken by deep valleys. In the south of the Townships, the valleys have been partly blocked by glacial drift (and locally

over-deepened) to form lakes Memphremagog, Massawippi, Magog, and many small lakes. Elsewhere the valleys are sunk into the uplands, as is the case of the Coaticook (below the town of that name), the Moe, the Eaton, and other rivers that flow towards the St. Francis (Fig. 7-2).

The drainage of the Eastern Townships has several anomalous features. It has already been shown that the main lowlands and the rivers associated with them are located on the least resistant rocks. It is paradoxical, therefore, to find that the largest rivers—the Chaudière, the Bécancour, the St. Francis below Lennoxville, and the Missisquoi below Highwater—flow in gorges across the resistant schists to find their way to the St. Lawrence Lowlands. A study of the drainage evolution reveals that before the Pleistocene glaciations, when denudation had not progressed far, other rivers had similar transverse courses (Fig. 7-3). Included in the streams that have since disappeared were a river that led from the Niger past Mount Orford; the Salmon River, which still rises near Mount Mégantic and once joined the central Nicolet; and a large river that followed a course indicated by Lake Mégantic, Lake St. Francis, and

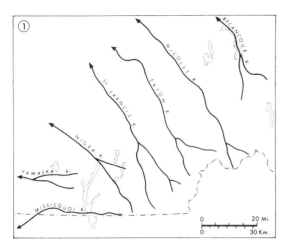

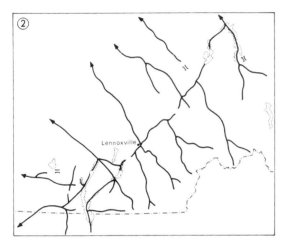

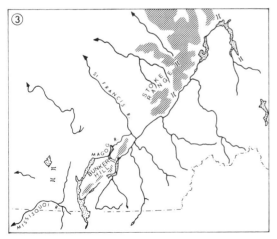

Fig. 7-3   Drainage evolution in the Eastern Townships. The residual hill ranges on the northwest side of the subsequent St. Francis River are shown in phase 3.

Black Lake, and which became eventually the Bécancour. All these rivers were captured and became tributaries of the St. Francis, as it extended along the softer rocks. When the rivers were beheaded, they left prominent wind gaps which mark their former position.

The maze of deep valleys produced by these events was further complicated during the Pleistocene glaciation, when deep erosion by the ice produced trough basins in some of the valleys, notably that of Lake Memphremagog. As the ice retreated, many of the valleys were filled with moraines and outwash sands. Conspicuous examples include the valley of the Chaudière around Vallée-Jonction, the upper Coaticook, and—perhaps most conspicuous of all—the valleys north of Cherry River near Magog, which have been almost obliterated beneath outwash sands.

The first part of the Eastern Townships to be uncovered as the Pleistocene ice sheet retreated was the area east of the Sutton Mountains. At that time, the ice front lay to the north of Magog and west of the Sutton Mountains, thus blocking the normal drainage to the St. Lawrence and Lake Champlain. Proglacial lakes filled the valleys to the south and east into northern Vermont, and from there the melt waters drained by channels which ultimately reached the Connecticut. After a further retreat, the ice margin halted for a brief period along the western side of the Notre Dame Mountains north of Thetford Mines; but by this time, the preglacial valleys were uncovered and the glacial lakes drained. Although this episode marked the last time a continental ice sheet covered the Eastern Townships, there are several indications that the climate once more deteriorated, leading to the formation (or possibly the survival) of a small icecap, which occupied the extreme southeast corner of the Townships along the Vermont–New Hampshire border.

Many conspicuous landforms were left by the ice. Probably the most prominent are the kame moraines and related valley outwash that often terminate in deltas formed in glacial lakes. Virtually all the larger valleys contain such a sequence. In many, when the rivers began eroding into the sand and gravel fill, they failed to uncover their former rock valleys and the resulting diversions are responsible for many waterfalls.

The redistributed fluvioglacial sands are also a significant feature of the southern piedmont, particularly between Yamaska Mountain and Quebec, where they are more than 12 miles wide. In most parts, the bedrock is buried beneath the thick drift, mainly sands. Only at a few places do low, parallel, rock ridges indicate the strike of the folded rocks beneath; dunes are widespread, and drainage is often poor.

Between the Chaudière and Lake Témiscouata

From Quebec to Rivière-du-Loup, the Canadian Appalachians are restricted to a zone not more than 30 miles wide between the St. Lawrence estuary and the Maine border. The core of the area is a zone of intensely folded schists of Cambrian or earlier age that are a direct continuation of the Sutton–Thetford rocks. These rocks underlie the Notre Dame Mountains, which exceed 3,000 feet at their highest part. The schists are pinched out towards Lake Témiscouata and the mountains become lower, eventually giving way to low rounded hills that project above the main upland level at about 1,250 feet. At several points in the northeast, the mountains are crossed by prominent valleys, which indicate a former southeastward drainage that was lost by capture to the St. Lawrence.

The piedmont northeast of the Chaudière is generally wider and rockier than in the Eastern Townships. A narrow coastal plain, in some places less than a mile wide, separates the St. Lawrence estuary from parallel, often till-covered ridges, which over a broad area are between 1,350 and 1,500 feet above sea level.

Gaspé–Northern New Brunswick

The Appalachian–Acadian Province east of Lake Témiscouata and the Madawaska–Saint John valleys, including the Gaspé Peninsula

and the northern plateau of New Brunswick, is exceptionally uniform in scenery. Broad upland surfaces of erosion are characteristic of many parts of the region.

The Gaspé region is developed mainly on Paleozoic sediments and igneous rocks that are contained in an elongated basin. The younger and generally weaker rocks of Devonian age occur along the axis that runs through the middle of the peninsula. The main rock formations outcrop in long curving zones parallel to the Gulf of St. Lawrence.

The middle of the peninsula is a flat, forest-covered upland, 1,300–1,800 feet above sea level and drained by consequent southeast-flowing rivers and subsequent streams developed along the strike of the rocks. The latter dominate the drainage pattern in the east. Within the basin are minor anticlines and synclines, which reach the sea in bays and headlands at the eastern end of the peninsula, where the coastline cuts across the strike of the folds. One of these headlands is Cape Gaspé, formed in Devonian limestone on the north side of Gaspé Bay. The lowlands and their submerged section under Gaspé Bay have developed through denudation by the Dartmouth, York, and Saint Jean rivers of the Gaspé sandstones and shales, also of Devonian age. Ten miles to the south is a smaller lowland, which results from the excavation of sandstones, shales, and conglomerates and has been partly submerged to produce Mal Baie. The bay separates broad, projecting Pointe Saint Pierre on the north side, composed of Mal Baie conglomerate, and on the south side the resistant, highly tilted limestones of the Murailles formation which are responsible for Percé Rock. Nearby Bonaventure Island is underlain by flat-lying sandstones and conglomerates.

Overlooking the central zone on the north is a fault-line scarp, at places nearly 2,000 feet high, which is the southern edge of the Shickshock Mountains. They are the highest part of Gaspé—and, indeed, of the Appalachians anywhere in Canada. They form a block from 5–15 miles wide and nearly 65 miles long, about 20 miles inland from the

Plate 7-2   An Appalachian surface of denudation: New Denmark, N.B.

Plate 7-3   Percé Rock and Bonaventure Island at the eastern end of the Gaspé Peninsula. Percé Rock is fossiliferous limestone of Devonian age, while Bonaventure Island is formed of Carboniferous clastic rocks. (Information Canada Photothèque. Photo by B. Beaver.)

north coast. The upper surface is a rolling highland with a general elevation of 2,500–3,000 feet, which rises over 3,500 feet in Mount Albert near the east end; beyond, on the far side of the Ste. Anne valley, is Tabletop Mountain, above which rises Mount Jacques Cartier to 4,160 feet. The highest summits are treeless and covered with felsenmeer. On the sides are small cirques. Both the north and south faces of the Shickshocks present a vast wall broken only by an occasional gap, such as the valley of the upper Rivière du Cap-Chat. The mountains are residual features that have survived long periods of denudation because of the great resistance to erosion of granites (which form the Tabletops) and volcanic rocks, which have been metamorphosed to schists elsewhere.

Between the Shickshocks and the coast are slates and quartzites that correlate with the rocks of the Appalachian piedmont elsewhere in Quebec. They form a rolling forest-covered upland surface at 1,500–2,000 feet, which reaches the sea in high cliffs; these have made the construction of a coastal road difficult and often impossible without detours inland. Many of the rivers flow on the upland in open valleys, in an east-west direction, before breaking out to the coast in narrow, steep-sided valleys.

In the southern sector of the peninsula is a belt of volcanic and clastic sediments 25–30 miles wide that dips towards Chaleur Bay. Because of the deep incision of the rivers, the relief is much rougher than in the central zone. In the Gaspé area, after the Acadian mountains were formed, there was a long period of erosion that ended in Carboniferous times, and sedimentation occurred in a basin with roughly the same position as present-day Chaleur Bay. These sediments, known as the Bonaventure beds, are mainly conglomerates with some sandstone; and they have remained unfolded. We have seen already that, in several parts of the Quebec Appalachians, the early rivers flowed across the southwest-northeast strike of the land. Nowhere is this clearer than immediately west of the Gaspé Peninsula, where the Matapédia, Petapédia,

Madawaska, and several smaller rivers traverse the uplands in steep-sided, usually flat-bottomed valleys, which are filled with glacial outwash deposited when the edge of the Pleistocene ice sheet lay to the northwest. All the main valleys are blocked by drift, and there are long deep lakes including lakes Matapédia and Témiscouata. Close to the main rivers, the bedrock is usually covered with bouldery drift and has been partly cleared of trees; but on the interfluves, slopes are steep and the forest-covered land is extremely wild. Traces of the elevated upland surfaces of Gaspé occur; but the land was probably never as flat as it is farther east, and these uplands are not a conspicuous feature of the landscape.

In extreme northern New Brunswick, strong dissection of quartzites has resulted in a complex area of hills. The hills end abruptly along the Restigouche, which—except for its upper section—is a secondary strike river. Together with its tributaries, the river has reduced the slates to a series of nearly level surfaces separated by low bluffs. The main upland is between 900 and 1,000 feet above sea level. The river must have meandered across the upland in broad sweeps until renewed uplift led to incision, during which the meanders were entrenched into the upland. The highway from Chaleur Bay to the Saint John River crosses these surfaces; and they are particularly prominent between Kedgwick and St. Quentin, where settlement has followed the clearing of the forest. At the southwest end of this upland, similar surfaces are related to the Saint John River—although here again the river is deeply incised, and flows below Grand Falls in a gorge. Above Grand Falls, the valley is flat-bottomed and, although deep, is more than a mile wide. After the retreat of the last ice sheet, the Saint John valley was filled with outwash deposits for many miles below Grand Falls. Downstream, this alluvium was quickly removed by the river; but at Grand Falls, the river meandered out of its former valley and was trapped on a rock ledge which effectively restricted erosion upstream. At the falls, the river tumbles back into its former channel.

The Saint John River has a complex geomorphological history (Fig. 7-4), many aspects of which have not yet been uncovered. From its source on the Quebec–Maine border to Edmundston, the river follows a subsequent course before it turns southeast along the line of the consequent drainage found in many rivers of northern New Brunswick and Gaspé. At Grand Falls, it turns south, but an earlier southeasterly course continued past this point and probably at one time took the river through a gap in the hills at Bluebell, across the Plaster Rock–Tobique plains, and then through a wide wind gap near Juniper. Why the river should turn south is not clear, particularly since in this section it is not closely adjusted to the structure. At Woodstock, the river resumes its southeastward course; but from here to the point at which it enters Long Reach, there have been several recent changes. The river once crossed the sandstone plain by a channel farther west than its course today, and it may have rejoined Long Reach below Nerepis.

Between Perth and Bath, the Saint John skirts the Central Highlands of New Brunswick. The heart of the Highlands are the granites intruded into the area during the Acadian Orogeny; together with some volcanic sediments and argillites, they constitute the highest part, with several peaks—including Mount Carleton—exceeding 2,500 feet. The summits are generally flat to rolling and treeless, and are covered with shattered rock fields interrupted by weathered rock knobs 25–50 feet high. Valleys cut through the main part of the Highlands near the source of the Tobique and Nepisguit rivers are more than

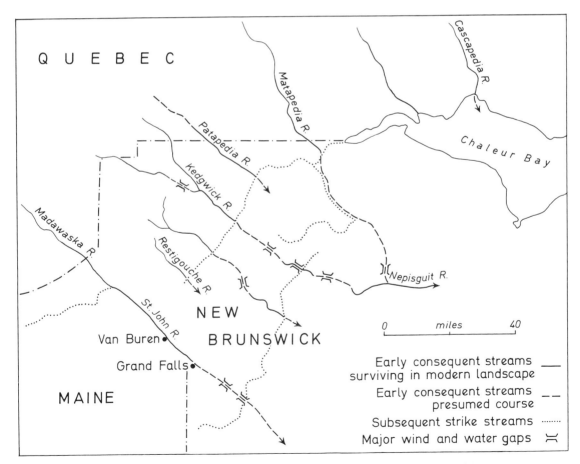

Fig. 7-4   Evolution of the river pattern in northern New Brunswick

1,000 feet deep, and at many points are occupied by lakes or filled with outwash sands. Through valleys, like those that occur in the Shickshocks, are also found in the Central Highlands and form spectacular, but largely inaccessible, gorges.

The Plains of Eastern New Brunswick, Prince Edward Island, and Northern Nova Scotia

In eastern New Brunswick, northern Nova Scotia, Prince Edward Island, and beneath the Gulf of St. Lawrence as far as the Magdalen Islands, the rocks are late Paleozoic sediments (on the mainland, predominantly of Pennsylvanian age). They are principally sandstones and shales, with some coal measures. The sediments were derived by erosion from the Acadian Mountains, and were deposited on land in a large, subsiding basin apparently centred over eastern Prince Edward Island. As compared with other rocks in the Maritimes, those of Pennsylvanian age are readily attacked by erosion, and they were denuded rapidly during Tertiary times. Today they underlie the most extensive plains in the Atlantic Provinces.

The great plain of eastern New Brunswick, together with its extension into northern Nova Scotia, is roughly a triangle with sides about 165 miles long. The base lies along Northumberland Strait and the apex is 40 miles southwest of Fredericton near Oromocto Lake. Within this large area, the rocks are generally flat-lying or low, wide, open folds. In the New Brunswick sector, landforms controlled by structure are not conspicuous; but the recurring southwest-northeast strike of many of the rivers in the southern part, including the Salmon and the Canaan, and the orientation of the shores of Grand Lake may reflect structures in the underlying basement rocks. A similar strike occurs in Indian Mountain near Moncton, where rocks of Mississippian age outcrop in a long narrow ridge, from which there are fine views of the plain to the north and the east end of the Vale of Sussex. In northern Nova Scotia, rather similar anti-

clinal structures of older rocks underlie parallel ridges, of which Springhill is the best known. They cross the plain from east to west and reach the sea in headlands such as Malagash Point.

Grand Lake, on the northeast side of the Saint John River near Gagetown, is the site of a broad shallow valley that entered the Saint John when its channel was much lower, probably by several hundred feet, than it is today. Subsequently, sea level and crustal changes caused the river level to rise; as it did, the main valley became filled with sediments, and the tributary valley of Grand Lake was blocked. Today the shallow body of water outlines the former sides of the valley. A similar origin accounts for Washademoak Lake.

In general, the plain is extremely flat and the scenery monotonous; but it is hardly surprising to find that, in such a wide area, there are often local differences. If for a moment the valleys are ignored, the remainder of the plain is found to vary from flat, often perfectly horizontal surfaces, such as occur near Northumberland Strait, to undulating and even hilly, but still smooth, terrain along the northern side. This latter element is particularly prominent in Gloucester County, where the surface of the plain rises from the coast to over 500 feet 25 miles inland in the vicinity of Allardville; the long gentle slopes are broken only by the deep valleys of the rivers. In contrast, south of the Miramichi, the plain is formed of low plateaus separated by broad flat-bottomed valleys. Although bedrock outcrops only along the margins of the plateaus, details of rock structure are probably responsible for their height and distribution. Except along the coast and in the middle of the plain, the rivers are everywhere entrenched. In the east, incision is only a few tens of feet, particularly near the margins; on the northwest side, it may reach several hundred feet. Indeed, the rivers have cut deep, open valleys into the former plain between Fredericton and the southwest Miramichi, and hills now separate the surviving plain from the Central Highlands. Many parts of the plain are poorly

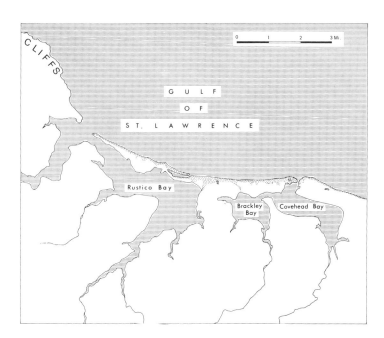

Fig. 7-5 The shores of Prince Edward Island

drained, and swamps and peat deposits are common. In the flattest parts, on the south side of Miramichi Bay and in the east of Gloucester County between Tracadie and Shippigan, are extensive treeless bogs.

In recent times, the sea has transgressed the plain, and long shallow estuaries have resulted. Pictou Harbour, Amet Sound, and Pugwash Harbour are some in Nova Scotia, and there are many in New Brunswick. In the lowest areas, particularly north of Shediac, an almost continuous sand and shingle offshore bar separates lagoons and long narrow estuaries from the open sea. The bars are often tied to low cliffs at one end and are then indistinguishable from spits; a very fine example virtually blocks off Buctouche Harbour. Marine constructional features are prominent on the Magdalen Islands, where the main islands are linked by sand spits several miles long. In a few localities, low sandstone plateaus reach the sea, forming magnificent cliffs. Along the southeast side of Chaleur Bay, an unbroken line of cliffs over 15 miles long and occasionally more than 100 feet high is centred on Grande-Anse, and somewhat lower cliffs are found from Point Escuminac to Point Sapin.

Prince Edward Island is geologically part of the same region as the New Brunswick Lowland, but the scenery differs in detail, mainly as a result of its more varied structure. All the rocks of the Island are Permo-Carboniferous in age, with sandstones and shales predominating. They are commonly red in colour, and weather to the rich red soil that is a well-known characteristic of the Island. Some of the sandstones are massive and produce ledges on hillsides, although buried deeply by soil; other sandstones are flaky and disintegrate into flat pebbles.

The structure is imperfectly known. It is clear, however, that it controls several of the major landforms of the Island. In some parts, the strata are flat-lying or gently dipping, and low plateaus and cuestas have formed. The northeast corner of the Island from St. Peters to East Point is one such plateau. A second is in the northwest, where a cuesta scarp up to 125 feet high extends with few breaks from near Tignish Point to West Point. The surface of the cuesta dips southeastwards to roughly the line of Highway 1. A basin structure underlies Hillsborough Bay, and the outer edge forms low scarps on either side of the entrance to Charlottetown Harbour and the coast from Orwell Bay to Prim Point.

No special structures appear to be associated with the two highest areas of the Island. In the southeast are the steep slopes of the hills around Caledonia, where narrow deep valleys are typically streamless and much of the area is under hardwood. The valleys, at least in part, have been modified by glacial melt waters; but the main relief results from the occurrence of conglomerates, which outcrop as boulder beds at many points.

The other high area is more extensive, and extends from the hills which are crossed by the Trans-Canada Highway near Churchill northwestwards to New London Bay. The highest part of the Island, south of Fredericton, exceeds 450 feet; the hills are deeply dissected by the headwaters of several streams. North of Fredericton, elevations are not as great; the slopes are smoother and often wooded, producing the very attractive valleys that enter New London Bay and the Southwest River.

Between the plateaus and the hills, the terrain is generally much lower and is normally rolling; in some parts, particularly west of Summerside, it is flat. An exception is east of the Hillsborough River; here, although the relief is lower than in the main hills, slopes are locally steep. A plateau about 200 feet high is crossed by valleys, the majority of which have a north-south orientation. Small valleys occurred in this area in preglacial times; it was the site of a wasting icecap at the close of the glaciation, and melt waters from the ice deepened the valleys and deposited sand and gravel ridges on their sides.

Details of the glacial history of the Island are obscure; but it is likely that, towards the close of Wisconsin time, ice from Cape Breton Island occupied the eastern third of the Island, while ice from New Brunswick and possibly farther north in the Gulf of St. Lawrence occupied the centre and west. Much of this ice seems to have melted *in situ*. One example has already been quoted; and rather similar conditions prevailed in the Tignish Peninsula, where the last remnants of ice were attacked by the sea, which at the time was locally about 75 feet higher than it is today.

The ice left several types of deposit. Most widespread is the ground moraine that forms a featureless mantle covering much of the bedrock of the Island. This varies in depth from 1 foot in many areas to over 50 feet at a few localities. The till varies in composition from predominantly sand to clay, depending

Plate 7-4   Sand dunes at Cavendish on the north coast of Prince Edward Island.

on the underlying rocks. Less common is ablation moraine let down from upper parts of the ice as it melted; this forms a coarser drift, often with rather steep slopes.

At first, when the ice sheets melted, the sea was higher than it is today; and for a short time, Prince Edward Island must have been a group of islands. But the land rose quickly, and at one period the shore extended beyond its present position. Most recently, the sea level has been rising, as it has in other parts of the Maritimes; and valleys have been submerged, producing long branching estuaries. The coastline is also being modified by erosion. Sandstone and siltstone cliffs have been attacked by waves, and even on sheltered coasts they are retreating at a rate of about a foot a year; they are probably retreating two or three times as quickly on the Gulf coast. At one time, the uplands along the north shore must have projected several miles into the sea as low headlands. Erosion has reduced them to straight cliffs that now form somewhat less than half the north coast. Originally, bays and estuaries separated cliff sections, but the growth of sand bars and spits has sealed off these waters from the open sea. The largest barrier bar is across Malpeque Bay, where Hog Island and the other islands are nearly 20 miles long. Rather better known, because of the ease of access through the National Park, are the spit-bar that projects west from Cavendish and almost closes New London Bay, and the Rustico Island–Brackley Point–Stanhope Beach complex that is a single discontinuous bar.

Major modifications by wave action are visible along the north shore. In contrast, along the protected Northumberland Strait shore, the estuaries are open to the sea; but even a brief trip along any part of this shore shows numerous sand bars of all types, tied islands, and longer spits.

The Southern Maritime Provinces

By the end of the Paleozoic era, crustal movements associated with mountain building had ended, except for a zone between the Bay of Fundy and Cape Breton Island. In this area, the basement rocks were disrupted by faulting into horsts and graben; mainly in the late Pennsylvanian period, locally in the Triassic period, desert sands, eventually to become sandstones, were deposited, and ultimately the whole faulted basement was buried. Today the horsts have been exhumed, and—with some modification by denudation—form the block mountains of the Caledonian Uplands, the Cobequid Hills, the Pictou–Antigonish Highlands, and Cape Breton Island (Fig. 7-6).

In southern New Brunswick, the main horst is the Caledonian Highlands. Smaller blocks form the hills on both sides of Long Reach, and between Passamaquoddy Bay and Saint John. Rocks in the Caledonian block are of Precambrian age and include volcanic rocks, metamorphosed sediments, and granites. For more than 50 miles, the north side coincides with the Waterford fault, resulting in an imposing and largely unbroken scarp 750–1,000 feet high which extends from near Loch Lomond, a few miles east of Saint John, to Shepody Bay. Along the south side, the highland falls abruptly to the Bay of Fundy; this margin may also be fault-controlled, although the pattern is more complex. The interior of the highlands is dominated by a surface of erosion—the Fundy Surface, at 1,000–1,200 feet—which for many miles is a continuous rolling upland, particularly in the east where it is broken only by occasional deep valleys.

The Vale of Sussex is on the north side of the Caledonian Highlands. It is a structurally controlled, denudational lowland drained by the Petitcodiac and Kenebecasis rivers. Weak sandstones have been differentially eroded from the centre and eastern sectors; but in the west, the structure is not simple, and examples of inverted relief occur.

Across Chignecto Bay from the Caledonian Highlands are the Cobequid Hills. These are comprised of a parallel sided block of resistant granite, volcanics, and partly metamorphosed sediments of mid-Paleozoic age, which have been denuded less rapidly than

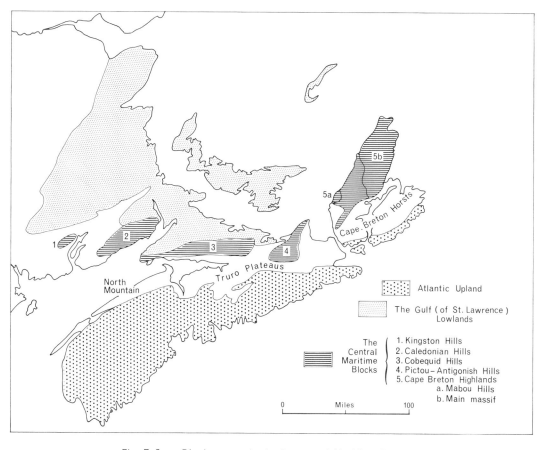

Fig. 7-6   Block mountains in the central Maritime Provinces

The legend reads:

Atlantic Upland

The Gulf (of St. Lawrence) Lowlands

The Central Maritime Blocks
1. Kingston Hills
2. Caledonian Hills
3. Cobequid Hills
4. Pictou–Antigonish Hills
5. Cape Breton Highlands
   a. Mabou Hills
   b. Main massif

0   Miles   100

Plate 7-5   Steeply tilted Triassic sandstones: St. Martins Head, N.B.

sandstones and other sedimentary rocks around its margins. The northern margin of the hills is an imposing fault-line scarp that is locally 600 feet high. It remains tree-covered to this day; and the forested slopes, broken by narrow, deep re-entrant valleys that are occupied by streams with many waterfalls, contribute to the scenic effect of the escarpment. The main highway and railway to Halifax pass through the hills at Wentworth, where the scarp reaches its finest development. West of Springhill, the scarp is lower; and in the extreme west, there is no difference in height between the hills and the Chignecto Plateau, which is part of the Northern Lowland.

The southern edge of the hills is also a fault-line scarp. It is best developed in the west where it overlooks Grenville Bay and Parrsboro. Farther east, between Bass River and Truro, it is less spectacular, for low sandstone plateaus intervene between the hills and the Minas Basin. The Cobequid Hills east of Parrsboro form a rolling upland between 950 and 1,000 feet above sea level that resembles the Fundy Surface. Low hills, which include the highest point in mainland Nova Scotia, Nuttby Mountain (1,204 feet), rise as monadnocks above the general level. There are also widespread remnants of a lower surface with a height of about 800 feet. The river valleys are deeply incised into the uplands, especially near the scarps, where the rivers flow in gorges.

East of a line from the Falls (south of Tatamagouche) to Truro, roughly along Highway 11, the mid-Paleozoic rocks are replaced by Mississippian sandstones and conglomerates. They have eroded more rapidly than the older rocks, and the valleys are larger, although traces of the high surface survive. There has been rather more settlement in this part of the Cobequids than elsewhere, and a combination of partly cleared valleys, wooded slopes, and hills produces an attractive landscape.

Although the Cobequid hills appear to be a major physical barrier across Nova Scotia, they are in fact crossed by valleys. Twenty passes can be recognized, although only one, the Parrsboro gap, has a stream flowing

through it at present. Other major valleys include the Wentworth gap, already mentioned, and the McGill Brook and west North River valleys. These valleys were initially produced by streams flowing across the Cobequid upland from the north, before northern Nova Scotia was reduced by denudation. Eventually, as the Northern Lowland developed, the headwaters of the south-flowing streams were diverted to Northumberland Strait and the valleys remained as wind gaps.

For a period at the close of the Pleistocene glaciation, the margin of the continental ice sheet lay along the north side of the Cobequids. Lobes of ice filled the valleys, and from them were deposited kame moraines, massive dumps of sand and gravel. They are particularly conspicuous at the northern entrance to the Parrsboro gap, in the Wentworth valley at Folly Lake, and south of Earlton. From the glacier margin, melt waters poured south through the valleys, carrying outwash sediments that today form terraces and elevated deltas where the rivers terminated in the sea. Perhaps the best example is at Debert.

The Pictou–Antigonish Highlands are separated from the Cobequid Hills by the Pictou Basin, where lowlands on Carboniferous sandstones and coal measures project south from Northumberland Strait. The highlands are triangular in plan, with the apex at Cape George. When seen from the narrow coastal plain along Northumberland Strait, the straight, steep scarp of the highlands resembles the edges of the other upland blocks; but there are few other similarities. The highlands have developed on slates, quartzites, and granites, probably of lower Ordovician age. The highest point, Eigg Mountain, is at 1,050 feet, but the mainland surface is closer to 750 feet. Deep valleys dissect the margins, and one, occupied by the Trans-Canada Highway, passes through the middle.

The upland blocks of the middle Maritimes are continued in the large mass of the Cape Breton Highlands, and in the smaller, usually tilted blocks that form the straight-sided hills around Bras d'Or Lake. Although relatively small, the latter are often very striking,

Plate 7-6   Sandstone cliffs of Cape Breton Island, N.S., being eroded by wave action. (Information Canada Photothèque. Photo by G. Hunter.)

as may be seen on the main Sydney highway from Baddeck that passes over one block between St. Ann's Bay and the Bras d'Or bridge.

The largest block, the Cape Breton Highlands, is one of the most scenic areas of eastern North America. The upland mass reaches the sea in a cliffed coast which makes access by land so difficult that only in the last two decades has a road been built around it. The core of the highland is formed of granitic rocks on which there is an upland surface that is between 1,500 and 1,600 feet above sea level in the centre. No roads penetrate into the highest part, which is comprised essentially of rock barrens, muskeg, and small, shallow, boulder-filled lakes. In the interior, the rivers flow in open valleys. Some miles from their source, they sink into the upland surface and within a short distance are

plunging between vertical walls to the sea. Around the margin, the upland drops gently by stages to about 1,250 feet, below which at many points there are cliffs.

The straight coasts of the highlands result from faulting in late Paleozoic and post-Carboniferous times, when the crust on both sides was depressed relative to the central granite core. Some of the sedimentary rocks still survive around the edges of the upland, producing highly coloured cliffs, particularly where "red beds" are present. At other points, the Carboniferous sediments appear to lie on the granites, as they do between Cape St. Lawrence and Cape North; here the hills are generally lower.

The most conspicuous fault is the Aspy fault, which extends for nearly 25 miles from Cape North southwestwards to beyond the source of the North Aspy River. The rocks on the southeast side of this fault have been depressed at least 2,000 feet, and sandstone and gypsum are preserved between granites on either side. The less resistant rocks have been partly removed by erosion, forming the plain around Dingwall and, where they are submerged, Aspy Bay. The main scenic elements of the Cape Breton Highlands, including the flat upland and the cliffs, were already in being before the last glaciation. The continental ice sheet appears to have swept over the Highlands at one time; but subsequently, they supported a small, independent icecap and, in the final stages, cirque glaciers lodged on the sides of the upland.

The Lowlands of the Middle Maritimes

It has already been noted that sedimentation in the Maritimes continued locally in basins into Triassic times. Rocks of this age include red sandstones, weakly cemented conglomerates, shales, and basaltic lavas. They occur on both sides of the Bay of Fundy in the Minas Basin–Cobequid Bay area and in a small outcrop on the shores of Chedabucto Bay, and they may underlie part of the continental shelf. The Triassic clastic rocks are easily eroded, and the Bay of Fundy is essentially a submerged lowland from which these rocks have been denuded; the sides of the bay—at least on the north side, where only scattered outcrops of Triassic rocks remain—are fault-guided.

Along the south side of the Bay, Triassic rocks underlie North Mountain and the Annapolis Valley. The former is 2–5 miles wide and 120 miles long from the southwest corner, where it is broken by sea-filled gaps between Brier and Long islands, to the curved hook of Cape Blomidon and Cape Split. The ridge is a series of Triassic basalt lava flows less than 1,000 feet thick, that dip to the northwest and reach the sea in cliffs which are from a few feet to over 100 feet high. The dip-slope on the Bay of Fundy side is crossed by small streams flowing in deep valleys. The steep

edge of the lava forms the North Mountain escarpment overlooking the Annapolis Valley.

Beneath the lava are sandstones and shales of the Annapolis Formation. Initially, they were protected by the lavas; but as the latter were removed by erosion, the weaker rocks were exposed and attacked rapidly by rivers, producing the present lowland. As subsequent streams developed on the Annapolis Formation and the lowland was extended, the initial streams which at one time crossed it at right angles were captured and diverted into the Cornwallis, Annapolis, and St. Mary's rivers. Later, the sea rose and submerged the lowest parts of the valleys. In the southwest, this led to the formation of St. Mary's Bay and the Annapolis Basin. The last river to breach North Mountain, the "Bear–Digby" River, was consequently drowned in its lower part. Near Middleton, the Mumford and Nictaux rivers for a time crossed to the Bay of Fundy close to Margaretsville. When they were captured, their former valleys were left as wind gaps leading through North Mountain.

The unique character of the Annapolis Valley is in part due to its position between North Mountain and the northern edge of the Atlantic Upland, known locally as South Mountain; and in part it results from the varied deposits within the lowland, many of which formed at the end of the Wisconsin glaciation, when ice from the *south* temporarily reoccupied the valley. As the ice melted, perhaps 10,000 years ago, kame moraines, outwash sands, and local lacustrine deposits together with wind-blown loess were left behind. The sea invaded the area and was for a time 60–90 feet higher than it is today, occupying long shallow estuaries which separated North Mountain from the uplands to the south. Today the sands remain largely uncultivated, particularly in the upper Cornwallis section, where they are most extensive. Elsewhere, however, the soils are some of the most valuable in the Maritimes, except where drainage is poor and peat bogs have developed. The largest of these, the Caribou bog, is being exploited for its peat.

The eastern arm of the Bay of Fundy—known in different sections as the Minas Channel, the Minas Basin, and Cobequid Bay—is a sunken section of a lowland of Triassic rocks. The rocks are preserved in a syncline between the Southern Upland and the Cobequid Hills to the north. The axis of the syncline runs from the middle of the Minas Channel, through Cape Blomidon at the east end of North Mountain, to a few miles east of Truro.

The basalt ridge is not continuous on the north side of the syncline, but has been breached for 10 miles west of Cape Split. It reappears south of Advocate Harbour and ends at Cape d'Or. A topographically and geologically similar broken ridge of basalt occurs on the north side of the Minas Basin opposite Cape Blomidon, where it forms Partridge Island near Parrsboro, Five Islands, and Gerrish Mountain. It is part of the same basalt formation as North Mountain and owes

its present position to faulting. Farther east, shales and sandstones of the Annapolis Formation are preserved in the Minas syncline. They are found along the north side of Cobequid Bay from Gerrish Mountain to five miles east of Truro; but on the south side of the bay, they are restricted to the headlands. Prior to the last glaciation, the coastline was much farther west and the sea was relatively lower than it is today; at the time, the Minas Basin and Cobequid Bay were a low plateau with an undulating surface, much as Economy Point is today. Fluvial denudation removed the surface rocks; and when the sea level rose, the lowest parts of the valleys were submerged.

The influence of the complex changes of sea level are clearly visible where the Annapolis Lowland passes beneath the Minas Basin. Spring tides in this area are exceptionally high, with a range exceeding 46 feet. The waters are shallow; and long, low sandstone island ridges, rising not more than a few feet

Plate 7-7   Partridge Island, constructed mainly of Triassic basalt, and linked to the mainland by a sand and shingle spit · Nova Scotia.

above high tide, formerly lay offshore. In the lee of the ridges, muds carried in by the high tides from the disintegration of shales along the coast were deposited and eventually stabilized by salt marsh. The larger marshes—Grand Pré, Booth Island, and Oak "Island"—have developed behind ridges linking them to the mainland. Other marshes occur along the estuaries of the streams entering the Minas Basin from the Annapolis Lowland, and small marshes are present on the rises of the St. Croix and Avon estuaries. When the Acadians first arrived from Port Royal in the seventeenth century, the marshlands provided the only treeless areas. But with the skills learnt by their ancestors on the marshlands of the lower Loire valley, the settlers were able to drain them and bring them into cultivation. The marshes have lost most of their natural characteristics, so that today it is often difficult to realize that the rich flat lands of areas such as Grand Pré were until recently salt marshes with deep tidal creeks and covered by the highest tides.

On the southwest side of the Minas Basin, drowned forests are visible at low tide. Radiocarbon dates show that the trees were living from 3,000–4,000 years ago, and that since then the land has been sinking at about 1 foot per century.

In several areas, the scenery is transitional between the lowlands and the upland blocks of the middle Maritimes, where low plateaus and hills have developed on Mississippian rocks which have been folded locally rather tightly. Included in this group are the plateaus in the St. Mary's watershed, the Antigonish hills and plains, and the sedimentary hills of western Cape Breton Island. In most parts, the bedrock has a deep drift cover which locally, as around Goshen, is strongly drumlinized.

The Atlantic Upland

A distinct physiographic region known as the Atlantic (or Southern) Upland is present along the Atlantic coast. The northern edge is formed by South Mountain and a conspicuous fault-line scarp which extends from the Minas Basin to Chedabucto Bay. The upland also occurs on Cape Breton Island, where it is less than 15 miles wide. It is essentially a tilted block, between 600 and 800 feet high in the inner side, and passing beneath the ocean in the southeast. The surface has been dissected by streams and in some parts, particularly between Halifax and the Avon estuary, is a mass of hills. The widest part of the upland is southwest of these hills, where it is developed about equally on metamorphic rocks of the Meguma group and on granite.

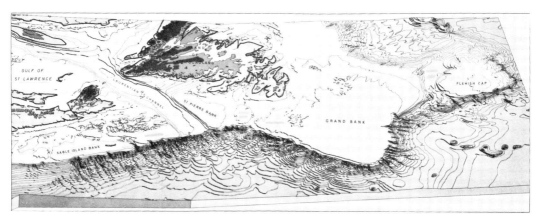

Plate 7-8   A relief diagram of part of the continental margin of the Atlantic Provinces. The continental shelf extends from the shoreline to the shelf break where the continental slope plunges down to the ocean basins. Note particularly the deep trench of the Laurentian Channel that separates Cape Breton Island and Newfoundland. (Reproduced with the permission of the Department of the Environment.)

The Meguma rocks are the oldest in the area, and consist of slates and quartzites of Ordovician age. They were folded during the Acadian Orogeny along generally northeast-striking axes, except in the Yarmouth area, where they are northerly. The Meguma group occurs primarily in the southwest and extreme east of the upland. They are generally lower than the granites; and where they are not buried beneath the glacial drift, the strike of the beds has imparted a strong grain on the terrain. This is particularly noticeable in the coastal areas, where it produces long narrow peninsulas and islands, such as those near Wedgeport and at Blue Rocks east of Lunenburg.

The massive granites are Devonian in age, having been intruded into the sediments during the Acadian Orogeny. The margins of the granites are commonly dissected by deep valleys; but in the central part, they form the typical Atlantic Upland, with an undulating and often rather flat terrain at an altitude of 625–725 feet from which rise steep-sided, bare-rock hills about 100 feet higher.

The evolution of the upland is still only partly understood, but it appears that the rocks exposed today were covered by other rocks, possibly the same Triassic sandstones that occur in the Annapolis Valley and the Minas Basin. Erosion removed these rocks from the highest land in the northwest and planed off the exposed granites. Later, the younger rocks were removed from the areas closer to the Atlantic, revealing the sub-Triassic surface, which has been only slightly changed since then. For a period in preglacial times, the sea level was lower than it is today, and the rivers flowed across the continental shelf. When the sea rose again, the lower parts of the valleys were drowned and long estuaries were formed. Some of these, such as the La Have estuary, are nearly 15 miles long; others, including the Bedford Basin and Halifax Harbour, have lost their former rivers by later drainage modifications.

The major elements in the landscape were already present before the last glaciation. As in so many other areas, the ice introduced limited changes into a landscape already very similar to that of today. At one time, it swept over all Nova Scotia, and the ice margin lay far out on the continental shelf, probably on the outer banks. After the retreat of the ice sheet, smaller icecaps survived at several places, one of which was on the Atlantic Upland southeast of Digby.

The most striking result of the glaciation was the development of extensive drumlin fields. In many parts of the Atlantic Upland, the till is thick and has been moulded into low drumlin hills. They are conspicuous where they have been cleared of forest and have a farm on the slopes, or where they are partly submerged, forming whale-backed islands. These are common in many lakes in the centre of the peninsula, and even more conspicuous in Mahone Bay. They are also prominent where they have been eroded by the sea and end abruptly in cliffs at the sea edge. This is particularly noticeable at the end of the peninsula between Lunenburg and the La Have River.

Although drumlins are found on all the main rocks of the upland, they are exceptionally well developed on the Halifax slates of the Meguma group. The largest field, containing several thousand drumlins, occurs in the western part of Lunenburg County. Smaller fields are present near the coast in Shelburne and Yarmouth counties, and another large group of drumlins is found in west Digby County.

Newfoundland

Newfoundland forms the northeastern terminus of the Appalachian geological and physiographic regions. This section of eastern Canada was adjacent to Europe before the two continents drifted apart, and the folded rocks of western Britain may at one time have been a direct continuation of those in Newfoundland.

The Appalachian orogenic storms left a lasting impression on Newfoundland by imposing a dominant southwest-northeast orientation on many of the major features. Exam-

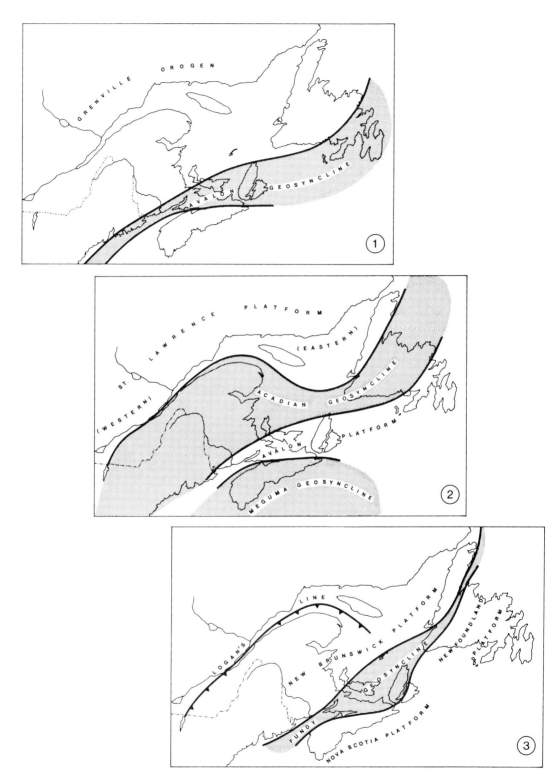

Fig. 7-7   The evolution of the Atlantic Provinces in early geological times: 1) Late Precambrian; 2) Ordovician period; 3) close of the Paleozoic period (after Poole)

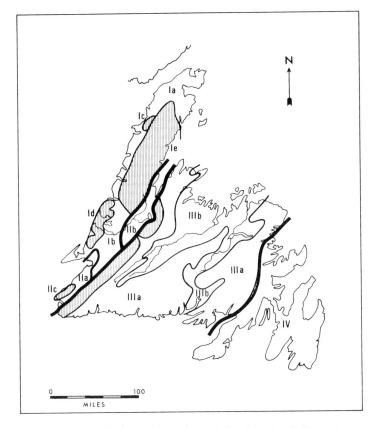

I   Western region
    a) West coast plains
    b) Humber hills
    c) Highlands of St. John
    d) Bay of Islands Hills
    e) Long Range
II Western Lowlands and Hills
    a) St. George–Codroy
        Lowlands
    b) Deer Lake–Grand Lake
        Lowland
    c) Anguille Mountains
III Central region
    a) Central Upland
    b) Notre Dame–Baie
        d'Espoir basins
IV Atlantic Upland

Fig. 7-8   The physiographic regions of Newfoundland. The main
western uplands are shaded.

ples of this can be found on the west coast, in the Deer Lake–White Bay depression, in the hill ridges of the Central Upland, and in the bays and peninsulas of the Avalon Peninsula.

The oldest rocks of the island occur in the Northern Peninsula. They are metamorphic rocks of Precambrian (Grenville) age, and they link this part of Newfoundland with the Canadian Shield across the Gulf of St. Lawrence. The first sign of the tectonic activity that led to the building of the northeastern Appalachian Mountains was the development of a geosyncline in the area of the present Avalon Peninsula during the late Proterozoic era (Fig. 7-7). The sediments deposited in the geosyncline eventually were converted into a platform. By the Ordovician period, a new geosyncline extended across the middle of Newfoundland between the northwestern

rocks and the Avalon platform. Towards the end of Paleozoic time, this geosyncline shrank in size and finally occupied a narrow strait from Cape Anguille to White Bay. At the same time, granites were intruded into the folded sediments of much of the central region.

The fourfold structural division into the western and Avalon platforms, and the main central and the smaller final geosynclines form a basis today for the division of Newfoundland into four physiographic regions (Fig. 7-8). In the west is a complex area of plateau massifs and small plains. East of this region is a zone of hills and lowlands, including the Deer Lake–White Bay Basin. In the centre of the island is a region corresponding mainly to the watersheds of the Exploits and Gander rivers, and developed principally on slates, greywackes, volcanics, and granites.

The fourth region lies southeast of a line from Fortune to Bonavista bays and includes the Avalon Peninsula.

The largest physiographic unit within the western region is a tilted plateau block of Precambrian rocks occupying the Northern Peninsula beyond Bonne Bay. The western edge, overlooking the Gulf of St. Lawrence, rises steeply from a narrow coastal plain of Paleozoic sediments, to an upland at 2,000–2,600 feet. The summit surface is gently undulating and, for the most part, barren; it drops by steps in a southeasterly direction to about 500–800 feet near White Bay, where it ends in cliffs. Short streams plunge off the plateau on the west side in narrow valleys that were over-deepened by valley glaciers in Pleistocene times. The plateau edge and the valleys produce some of the most spectacular scenery in eastern Canada south of the Arctic islands. The northern part of the peninsula, particularly the lowland around Hare Bay, is developed on limestone and contains numerous solution hollows and minor karst features.

South of Bonne Bay, four small massifs are preserved on either side of the Bay of Islands: on the north, separated by Upper Trout Pond, are the North Arm–St. Gregory Highlands and Table Mountain; and on the south, the Lewis Mountains and the Blow-me-down Hills. Topographically, the massifs, with their flat upper surfaces at 2,300–2,600 feet, resemble the Northern Plateau; the margins are frequently precipitous and are gashed by deep, glacier-modified valleys. It has been suggested that the rocks of these plateaus are *klippen*—great masses of folded rock, which were thrust as much as 100 miles from the southeast during the Paleozoic mountain-building period. Around the plateaus are upland areas, developed on Ordovician clastic and carbonate rocks; here denudation has progressed much further, leaving hills about 1,000–1,500 feet high.

Valleys are a conspicuous feature of the western region, even though some are only a few miles long. The largest river, the Humber, rises on the barren, flat, summit surface of the Northern Peninsula near the west coast.

As it flows towards the eastern edge of the plateau, it enters a deeply incised valley, which in turn opens out into the wide Deer Lake–White Bay Lowland. Below Deer Lake, the valley narrows, and the river passes through a gorge before entering the Humber Arm of the Bay of Islands. The origin of the gorge is obscure. The middle Humber may, at one time, have flowed in the reverse direction towards White Bay; later, either it was captured by a resequent stream from the Bay of Islands, or the drainage divide was breached by a Pleistocene glacier flowing towards the sea.

The second region, corresponding closely to the final geosyncline, occupies a narrow belt between the Codroy Valley and White Bay. The rocks, including sandstone, conglomerates, and gypsum, have been denuded more rapidly than most in western Newfoundland; they are divided into two by an upland massif between the Bay of Islands and Grand Lake. The southwestern sector is dominated by the Cape Anguille Mountains, a fault-guided block of clastic rocks that have been folded into an extended arch. The summit surface is undulating and stepped at a height of 1,300–1,750 feet; the margins are deeply broken by streams. The northeast sector of the belt is the Deer Lake–Grand Lake Lowland.

The western margin of the Central Upland is a conspicuous fault-guided scarp in the southern part, where it is known as the (southern) Long Range. From Grand Lake northwards, the edge is somewhat lower and is broken by many valleys. The (southern) Long Range is frequently described as part of the Long Range of the Northern Peninsula. Although there are close similarities between this plateau and those of the western region, in this account it is treated as the steep uptilted western edge of the Central Upland.

The Central Upland resembles an elongated and tilted saucer, with the low northeast side removed where it dips beneath the sea to form the islands of Notre Dame Bay. The highest parts of the saucer are the barren western and southern rims, which reach over

Plate 7-9   Contorted Ordovician shale, possibly developed during massive thrust-faulting in the Taconian Orogeny: Port au Port, Newfoundland. (Geological Survey of Canada, Ottawa.)

2,000 feet in the southwest but decrease to 1,500 feet in the east. The rims are largely developed on granitic intrusions, while eugeosynclinal facies, greywackes, volcanics, shales, and sandstones are concentrated in the interior and the northeast. The basins of the Exploits and Gander rivers form the lowest sections. The landscape contains numerous lakes; flat topography is broken by occasional isolated hills and ridges that rise above the general surface, particularly in the granite sectors.

The southeast region is underlain by clastic sediments and volcanics that were metamorphosed to varying degrees at the close of the Precambrian era. Shales and other rocks of early Paleozoic age are preserved in synclines and basins overlying the Precambrian rocks. The present physiography is strongly controlled by the Precambrian structures, with the major bays corresponding to downfolds. At some stage in the past, the surface was levelled, and subsequent crustal elevation and

ice action are responsible for the flat, lake-covered rocky uplands that reach the coast in high cliffs. An early, preglacial drainage apparently flowed towards the east, and the ice deepened many of the valleys after the drainage was disrupted.

Flat upland surfaces closely resembling surfaces in New Brunswick and Nova Scotia are especially conspicuous on the plateaus of western Newfoundland, but they are found in many parts of the island. Twenhofel, who had discussed their origin as early as 1912, returned to the island with MacClintock in the late 1930s, and they subsequently interpreted the surfaces as peneplains that had been elevated and tilted towards the east. Three separate peneplains were identified: in the west was the Long Range peneplain, preserved on the plateau summits at about 2,000 feet; a middle surface found in the high valleys of the west coast was described as dipping at a rate of 2 feet per mile towards the Avalon Peninsula, where it survives on the hills at an altitude of about 700–800 feet; a third level, the St. Lawrence peneplain, drops from 500–1,000 feet in the west to 350–400 feet in the southeast. This interpretation has been questioned in the west, where closer inspection suggests that many of the apparently dipping upland surfaces are in reality multiple stepped horizontal surfaces. It is also possible that the denudation surfaces in the Notre Dame Basin and the Avalon Peninsula are modified exhumed surfaces, resembling several in the Maritime Provinces.

Newfoundland was completely submerged by Pleistocene ice. Until recently, it was believed that the ice was part of the Laurentide ice sheet; but it is now recognized that during the final few thousand years of glaciation, and possibly throughout the Wisconsin, the island supported an independent icecap. The only exception was in the extreme north, where Labrador ice crossed the Strait of Belle Isle. The western margin of the Newfoundland icecap was in contact with Labrador ice in the Gulf of St. Lawrence; off the south and east

coasts it calved directly into the Atlantic Ocean. During the final stages of deglaciation, the coasts—except in the far north—were clear of ice, and valley glaciers flowed off the western uplands through deep valleys to the sea. After this phase, and almost certainly during earlier glaciations, cirque glaciers occupied hollows on the sides of the plateaus. The last ice vanished from the north coast rather less than 11,000 years ago.

With the retreat of the glaciers, the sea advanced into the lowlands. The transgression was small in the south and east, but appears to have covered much of the far northern lowland around Hare Bay, where the land has subsequently risen 400 feet.

Postglacial modifications of the landforms have been few. Where the coasts are developed in unconsolidated sediments, cliffs have been formed and shore material reworked into bars and other construction features. Elsewhere, changes have been slight; most conspicuous are the peat bogs, which are widely distributed in all parts of the island.

Selected Readings

Alcock, F. J., "Geology of Chaleur Bay Region", *Geol. Surv. Can. Mem.* 183, 1935, 146 pp.

Bird, J. B., "Some Aspects of the Geomorphology of the Eastern Townships of Quebec", *Rev. Géogr. Montréal*, Vol. 24, 1970, pp. 417–429.

"The Denudational Evolution of the Maritime Provinces", *Rev. Géogr. Montréal* (in press).

Cameron, H. L., *Glacial Geology and the Soils of Nova Scotia* in Legget, R. F., *Soils in Canada*, Toronto, University of Toronto Press, 1961, pp. 109–114.

Gadd, N. R., "Moraines in the Appalachian Region of Quebec", *Geol. Soc. Am. Bull.*, Vol. 75, 1964, pp. 1249–1254.

Goldthwait, J. W., "Physiography of Nova Scotia", *Geol. Surv. Can. Mem.* 140, 1924, 179 pp.

Howie, R. D., and L. M. Cumming, "Basement Features of the Canadian Appalachians", *Geol. Surv. Can. Bull.* 89, 1963, 18 pp.

McDonald, B. C., and W. W. Shilts, "Quaternary Stratigraphy and Events in Southeastern Quebec", *Geol. Soc. Am. Bull.*, Vol. 82, 1971, pp. 683–698.

Poole, W. H., "Tectonic Evolution of Appalachian Region of Canada", *Geol. Assoc. Can. Spec. Paper* 4, 1967, pp. 9–51.

Prest, V. K., and D. R. Grant, "Retreat of the Last Ice Sheet from the Maritime Provinces – Gulf of St. Lawrence Region", *Geol. Surv. Can. Paper* 69-33, 1969, 15 pp.

8

The Great Lakes–St. Lawrence Lowlands

Around the southern edge of the Canadian Shield in Ontario and Quebec is a belt of lowlands that is divided by a southeastern projection of the Shield along the Frontenac Axis in eastern Ontario into a Great Lakes sector and an eastern Ontario–southern Quebec sector. The latter region is known generally as the St. Lawrence Lowlands.

The St. Lawrence Lowlands

The St. Lawrence Lowlands extend 250 miles from Arnprior and Perth west of Ottawa to a few miles below Quebec City (Fig. 8-1). The rocks of the lowlands were deposited in early Paleozoic times on a sinking continental margin of Precambrian rocks, between a major land mass, the Canadian Shield, to the north and the Appalachian geosyncline with its vulcanism and recurring mountain building to the southeast. Much later geologically, when all of southeast Canada was land and was being eroded, the lowland rocks were more easily denuded than the rocks of the Shield and the Appalachians; and today they are closer to sea level than the others, as well as often being buried deeply by drift.

As the platform of Precambrian rocks foundered in the Cambrian, sands were washed over it from the Shield, and eventually the hilly landscape was buried beneath the Potsdam sandstone. Movements in the basement of the platform subsequently raised the Precambrian rocks along the Beauharnois Axis, which extends from east of Lachute through southwestern Quebec to the Adirondacks. Along the axis, Precambrian rocks penetrate the sedimentary rocks of the lowlands on both sides of the Ottawa River at Lake of Two Mountains to form Rigaud and Oka "mountains". A third and lower outcrop produces the rough terrain near St. Andrews East. In Quebec, the Potsdam sandstone is exposed at the surface only near the Beauharnois Axis, although it underlies much of the lowlands. It is especially prominent in Chateauguay County close to the Adirondacks, where a broad area is a drift-free sandstone plain.

The sandstones buried the inequalities of the platform; and when early in the Ordovician period seas again flooded the platform, a gentle, flat surface was present for the new deposition. Throughout much of the Ordovician period, the sea oscillated across the lowland. This led to the deposition of limestone, often dark blue or black in colour; of dolomite, particularly early in the transgression; and, towards the end, of considerable thicknesses of shale. The Ordovician dolomite, which can be clearly seen above Beauharnois, and the limestones, including the Trenton visible on the sides of Mount Royal, are relatively resistant to erosion and occur at the surface mainly in the west of the lowland. Indeed, close to the Frontenac Axis they commonly form bare, rather ill-drained, limestone plains and low plateaus.

East of Montreal, shales predominate, although natural exposures are rare as they are buried under thick drift deposits. This distribution results from the thinning out and eventual disappearance of the lower beds towards Quebec and the deformation of the younger sediments. The latter comprise a canoe-shaped basin, with the synclinal axis extending from near Quebec in a southeast and southerly direction towards the New York border near Lake Champlain. The youngest rocks, the Queenston shales, out-

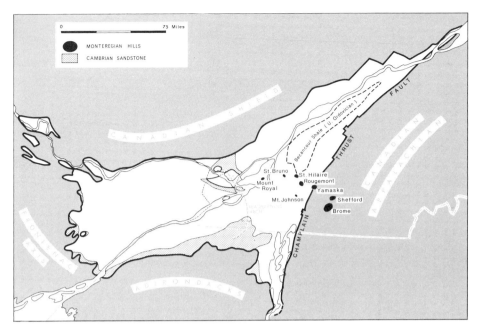

Fig. 8-1   The St. Lawrence Lowlands

crop in a broad zone immediately east of the St. Lawrence River from Montreal to Donnacona.

Sedimentation continued after the Ordovician period, but the later rocks have long since vanished through erosion, except for fragments that were incorporated into volcanic rocks at several points in the lowlands.

It has already been shown that intense mountain building occurred in the Appalachian geosyncline on three occasions during the Paleozoic era. These events may have led to faulting in the lowlands; for many faults— the majority oriented parallel or at right angles to the edge of the Shield—have been traced, although they are not usually visible in the landscape.

During the Cretaceous period, the St. Lawrence Lowlands experienced deep-seated stresses in the basement rocks. West of Ottawa, these resulted in the down-faulting of the Bonnechere graben, in which today Paleozoic limestone is preserved, surrounded by Shield rocks. Farther east, igneous rocks penetrated the sedimentary rocks of the lowlands along a line extending from the middle of Oka Mountain across Logan's Line into the

Appalachians as far as Mount Mégantic. It is not known whether the intruded gabbro and syenite reached the surface, resulting in volcanoes, although in some cases it certainly did not. After igneous activity ceased, long-continuing erosion removed the highest igneous rocks and surrounding sedimentary rocks, until today the intrusions project as hills above the more easily eroded sedimentary rocks. Named the Monteregian Hills by F. D. Adams in 1904, five hills—Mount Royal, St. Bruno, St. Hilaire, Rougemont, and Mount Johnson—are the most conspicuous landforms in the Montreal Plain, with a sixth, Yamaska, a little east of Logan's Line.

After the cessation of igneous activity, no recognizable deposits were left in southern Quebec until the Pleistocene glaciations. It was during this period, however, that the scenery of the St. Lawrence Lowlands developed its main characteristics. It is true that the Ice Ages were again to modify it in detail; but by the end of the Pliocene epoch, the lowlands already had the main elements we can recognize today. Any reconstruction of the Tertiary events must be considered extremely tentative. Early in the era, the present surface was buried beneath at least 3,000 feet of rock that has since been removed. At first, the lowlands were not recognizable, because the sedimentary rocks overlapped onto the Shield. The main rivers must have risen far to the north and northwest, and may even have continued across New England as precursors of the Connecticut and other present-day rivers.

As denudation proceeded, the lesser resistance to erosion of the lowland rocks as compared with those to the north and southeast became apparent, and major subsequent streams were concentrated in the lowlands. For a time, the lowlands were more extensive than today, and included the upper and middle St. Lawrence estuary. Detailed studies suggest that the St. Lawrence Valley between Lake Ontario and Gaspé is, on the geological time scale, a youthful valley. The central sector—that is, the part we call the St. Lawrence Lowlands—only recently began to drain to the Gulf of St. Lawrence; previously, it was drained by a river with a very different course, perhaps between the Green Mountains and the Adirondacks to a forerunner of the Hudson River. Below Quebec, another river, the Proto-St. Lawrence, flowed northeastwards

to the vicinity of Anticosti before joining a major southeast-flowing river that cut through the Appalachians in the area of the Gulf of St. Lawrence and Cabot Strait. Later, the estuary river captured the upper river and diverted it to the sea past Quebec. This rather complex story accounts for the way in which the St. Lawrence Lowlands *rise* from Lake St. Peter *downstream* to Quebec, and explains why the river becomes entrenched in this area.

Although it is certain that the St. Lawrence Lowlands experienced several glaciations, no direct evidence has been found for a glaciation earlier than the Wisconsin. At several points along the St. Lawrence River, around Lake St. Peter and in the Chaudière Valley, glacial till lies beneath non-glacial deposits, which in turn are covered by other glacial sediments. It is assumed that the bottom till was formed during an early Wisconsin glaciation. This was followed by a warmer period lasting perhaps 5,000–7,000 years. The climate then deteriorated, and the flood plain of the St. Lawrence was occupied briefly by a lake. Shortly afterwards, a glacier covered the area and ice swept through as far as the Atlantic. The events that followed are only

Plate 8-1   Two of the Monteregian Hills in the St. Lawrence Lowlands, viewed from a third: St. Hilaire, Quebec.

vaguely known. Possibly the ice retreated again, only to advance once more; but this speculation is based on what is known to have been occurring elsewhere at the time.

Towards the end of the Wisconsin, about 13,000 years ago, the first ice-free areas appeared in Gaspé and in the extreme southeast of Quebec (Fig. 8-2). In the Eastern Townships, this led to the ponding of long narrow glacial lakes (see Chapter 4). As the ice sheet thinned, the ice front retreated and lay along the rising ground south and southeast of the St. Lawrence Lowlands; around its edge, melt water drained into the Champlain Basin and Eastern Townships lakes. The ice withdrew from the south of the lowlands, and for a brief period the latter was occupied by a lake. For a short time, ice in the lower St. Lawrence blocked the sea from entering the lowlands;

but it quickly disintegrated, and the sea invaded, forming the Champlain Sea about 11,800 years ago. The ice front retreated to the north, only to advance again within a few hundred years. On this occasion, however, it reached the lowlands at only a few points, producing a conspicuous terminal moraine that extends from St. Raymond, 25 miles to the west and then roughly parallel to the St. Lawrence through the village of St. Narcisse (from which it takes its name), and across the St. Maurice near Shawinigan Falls to St. Gabriel de Brandon (Fig. 8-3). From there, it may be traced across the Shield to close to the vicinity of Ste. Agathe and St. Jovite. The moraine is normally a single embankment of water-sorted material from 10–50 feet in height. Occasionally, large deltas were formed at the mouths of glacial streams along the

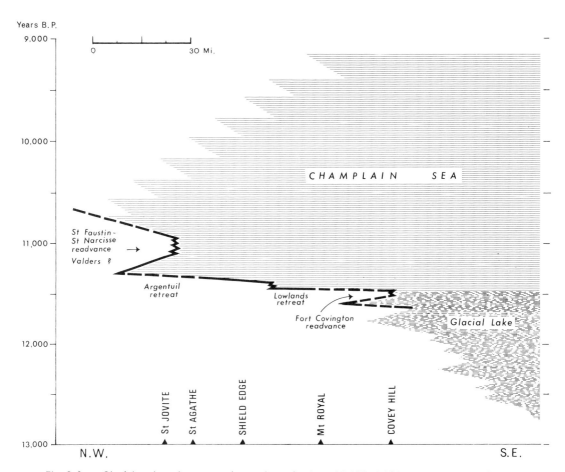

Fig. 8-2   Glacial and marine events in southern Quebec, 13,000–9,000 years ago (after Parry)

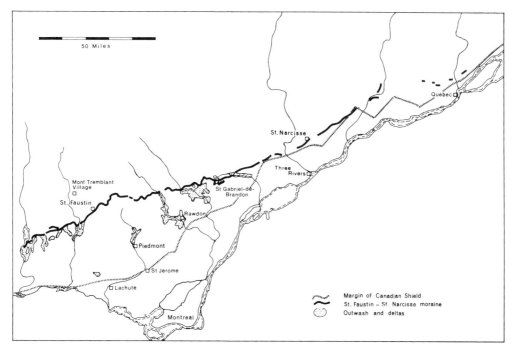

Fig. 8-3   The St. Faustin–St. Narcisse moraine (after Parry)

edge of the Champlain Sea. The largest of these is at St. Gabriel. Then, as the climate once more improved, the ice retreated and never again approached the St. Lawrence.

Several major modifications to the pre-glacial landscape were made by the ice sheet. Over large areas, glacial clays were deposited. These are rarely prominent today, however, as they have been buried by Champlain Sea and river sediments. The most extensive are in Chateauguay and Huntington counties in southwest Quebec, where the till is faintly ridged in a southwest to northeast direction; and in eastern Ontario, where glacial clays cover a large area north of the St. Lawrence River. Near Cornwall, and between Ottawa and Kemptville, the tills are drumlinized. Eskers are rare in the lowlands, although it is possible that they once existed and were destroyed by the sea or buried by deposits; esker ridges are found near Kemptville and Baudette. Sand and gravel ridges found at several points in the Montreal Plain may also have a fluvioglacial origin.

The Champlain Sea flooded almost all the lowlands, the only unsubmerged land being the tops of the Monteregian, Rigaud, and Oka hills, which appeared as small islands in the sea. The crust was already rising rapidly when the sea broke into the lowlands; and although the readvance of the ice may have caused fluctuations, the rebound was fast. Within less than 5,000 years, it had risen to its present level. The highest traces of the sea are now 500 feet above modern sea level in the southern part of the lowlands and 750 feet in the Laurentian valleys.

In the deepest waters of the Champlain Sea, marine and estuarine clays and silts were deposited. These now form monotonously flat, ill-drained plains. At first, the main ice sheet was still not far to the north, and there were small icecaps in the uplands south of the lowlands. Great quantities of sand were brought into the sea by the rivers; and as the water retreated, the resulting deltas extended into the lower parts of the plains until eventually very nearly the entire lowland area must have been a great sand plain. Some of the individual deltas are very extensive, particu-

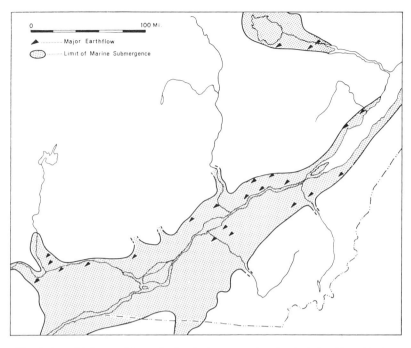

Fig. 8-4   Major earthflows in the St. Lawrence Lowlands (after Hortubise)

larly the delta of the St. Maurice, which extends from Shawinigan Falls almost to Three Rivers, and the St. Francis and the Chaudière deltas. Many of the deltas were at first miniature deserts covered with sand dunes which became stabilized as vegetation colonized the area. The dunes were reactivated during settlement in the late eighteenth and nineteenth centuries, when extensive felling of the forests bared them once again to the wind.

As the Champlain waters withdrew, they ceased to be marine: first, they became estuarine, and then for a brief space of time a lake occupied part of the lowlands. The rivers flowing across the sand plains towards Quebec rapidly cut down through the sands, exposing the buried marine clays. Initially, many of the rivers, particularly the Ottawa, had several channels; but with time, they became integrated, leaving dry sand plateaus that were ultimately covered with pine trees and separated by channels, several miles wide, of ill-drained marine clays. In some cases, the channels were still occupied by small streams. In others, there was no regular stream system and peat bogs developed. Sand plateau scen-

ery is well developed between Ottawa and Hawkesbury, and east from Lachute north of Montreal Island. The sides of the channels often rise 50 feet or higher; and, together with bluffs cut by the Champlain Sea and Lake "Montreal", they form breaks in the otherwise flat lowlands.

At first, the rivers flowed entirely over superficial deposits. But as they cut down, they reached bedrock, and rapids began to appear where the rock was unusually resistant. Below the rapids, the clays and sands were swept away by water and ice, and wide, shallow plunge pools were formed; the most conspicuous are the La Prairie Basin below the Lachine rapids and the Chambly Basin on the Richelieu.

As the rivers attained their present channels, the lowlands—except for vegetation changes—became very much as they are today. Drainage was often poor, and the flat lands and peat swamps expanded. In some areas, notably the Alfred Marsh of eastern Ontario, and in southwestern Quebec close to the United States border, they covered wide areas. Not everywhere are the lowlands unchanging, for conspicuous earthflows have developed along bluffs and river banks where sand overlies clay. More than 700 have been mapped (Fig. 8-4); many are several hundred feet long and have destroyed good farmland and associated buildings. A flow at Nicolet in 1955 destroyed 6 acres, killed 3 people, and did $5,000,000 of damage. Sometimes, they are much larger: a prehistoric earthflow in Alfred Township modified 15 square miles, and another near Kenogami dated at A.D. 1400–1500 covered 8 square miles. The cumulative effect is often considerable, and the Maskinongé Valley east of St. Gabriel has been almost filled by flows from the side terraces. The earthflows develop in Champlain Sea sediments from which the salts have been leached, a process that increases their sensitivity and decreases the shear strength of the clays (Fig. 8-5).

Southern Ontario

One of the most easily recognized physiographic divisions of Canada is the Southern Ontario Lowland, the rich agricultural area bounded by the Great Lakes on the south and west and the Canadian Shield on the northeast. Although a distinct unit in Canadian eyes, in reality it is only part of a much larger Great Lakes region that reaches even fuller development in the United States. If the border is ignored, it may be traced without significant break, but with continuous minor changes, into southern Manitoba.

The fine detail of the soils and landscape of southern Ontario is the work of ice and glacial lakes, but the framework to which these modifications were added is far older and reflects the long evolution of the region in preglacial times. In the simplest terms, southern Ontario is a scarpland subdued by events in the Pleistocene epoch, until in many parts the scarps are no longer a significant element in the landscape.

As in many other parts of Canada, the basement underlying the sedimentary rocks of southern Ontario is the Canadian Shield. The buried Shield and the overlying rocks in southern Ontario dip southwestwards at a few feet per mile, until in the extreme southwest the Shield is more than 4,700 feet below the surface. Although southern Ontario is part of the great stable interior of North America, the basement has been marked by depression and uplift, which have developed basins and domes. It is perhaps easiest to begin the story in Algonquin Park, a domed area of the Shield from which arches extend southeast in an exposed section by the Frontenac axis to the Adirondacks and by a buried section southwestwards past Dundalk to Windsor. Although the latter is invisible, the change in direction of the Niagara escarpment and the high ground of the Ontario "island" may reflect this hidden structure. Southwards in the United States, the same feature becomes part of the Cincinnati Arch and the Nashville

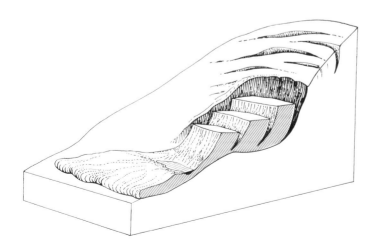

Fig. 8-5 A typical earthflow in the Champlain sediments of the St. Lawrence Lowlands

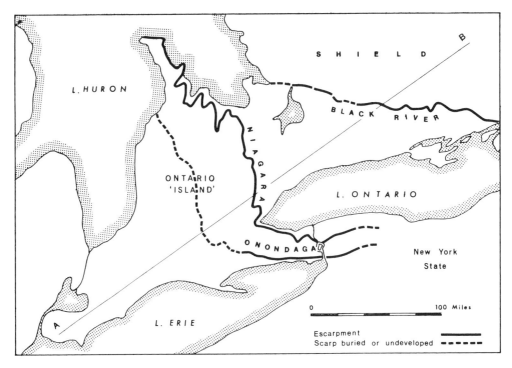

Fig. 8-6   The scarps of southern Ontario

Dome. To the west and overriding the effect of the arch is the Michigan Basin, which experienced almost continuous sedimentation in the Paleozoic era, while the arch areas had intermittent sedimentation.

The oldest sediments deposited in the Paleozoic seas were sands. These are no longer exposed on the surface, although they are found at depth in southwestern Ontario (Figs. 8-6 and 8-7). They were followed in the Ordovician period by deposition of dominantly calcareous rocks which have in contemporary exposures proved to be generally resistant. The Black River limestone, as it is called, overlaps onto the Canadian Shield from the Penetang Peninsula to east of Kingston, and locally forms a scarp 25–50 and occasionally 75 feet high from which it is possible to look out northwards over the extremely flat Shield. The scarp occasionally breaks up into several small scarps. In other places, isolated masses of limestone that have been detached by erosion from the main mass form plateau outliers on the Shield. Although

limestone outcrops in extensive plains northeast of Lake Simcoe, well-developed scarps are restricted to the north side of the Kawartha Lakes and occur intermittently eastwards as far as Kingston.

Between the scarp and the Shield, there is commonly a depression in which there are small lakes and one extensive body of water, the Kawartha Lakes. Resistant beds also occur in the overlying Trenton limestone, and low scarps are found locally north of Lindsay and Peterborough.

Although the Trenton and associated formations occur in a zone nearly 50 miles wide, outcrops are in many parts restricted to the vicinity of the Shield as the limestone becomes progressively buried beneath drift to the southwest. An exception is from the Bay of Quinte eastwards to the Thousand Islands, where limestone pavements are widespread.

The Trenton seas ended with a brief withdrawal, at least in the Georgian Bay and Manitoulin areas, and this in turn was succeeded by a marine episode in which muds

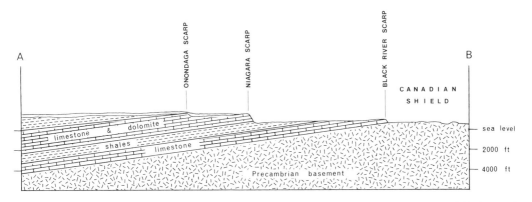

Fig. 8-7   A geological section across southwestern Ontario showing the major scarps and the increasing depth of the Shield in the southwest corner of the province

Plate 8-2   The back scarps of the South Nation River (eastern Ontario) landslide of May 16, 1971. (W. J. Eden, Division of Building Research, National Research Council.)

(now shales), sands, and limestones were deposited. The shales dominate the lowlands between the early Ordovician limestone and the foot of the Niagara escarpment. The rocks in general have been the weakest in southern Ontario, and they are rarely exposed on the surface but are covered by thick drift deposits. In the Toronto area, they are visible in the bottom of ravines; and in the Don Valley, they have been quarried for brick manufacturing. At the close of Richmond time, during which the Queenston red shale was deposited, the sea withdrew from southern Ontario. An important unconformity separates the Ordovician and the Silurian beds that follow.

The Silurian beds of southern Ontario are exceptionally well known, as they are exposed in the Niagara escarpment and the Niagara gorge (Fig. 8-8). The most resistant member is the Clinton limestone in the middle of the section, which forms a ledge about 15 feet above river level in Niagara Falls. Above these formations is shale and then the cap rock of Lockport dolomite. At the falls, this is a grey, tough crystalline dolomite about 66 feet thick. The falls retreat as the shales and sandstones beneath the hard dolomitic cap are undermined by spray, currents, and water-driven boulders. The recession of the falls from the Niagara escarpment has left a gorge nearly 7 miles long. At the present time, there are two falls: the American Falls and the Canadian or Horseshoe Falls, separated by Goat Island. The drop to the water is about 165 feet, and there is a somewhat greater submerged face below the water. Below the falls, the gorge is 300–400 yards wide. On the Canadian side, they have retreated nearly 300 yards in two centuries. If the present rate of retreat is maintained, it will be 25,000 years before the falls retreat to Lake Erie and the lake is substantially lowered. The rate of retreat has, however, decreased; and even if man did not interfere with the falls, it would undoubtedly take very much longer to reduce them.

It was once thought that the Niagara gorge was a product of postglacial retreat of the falls from the Niagara escarpment, but it is

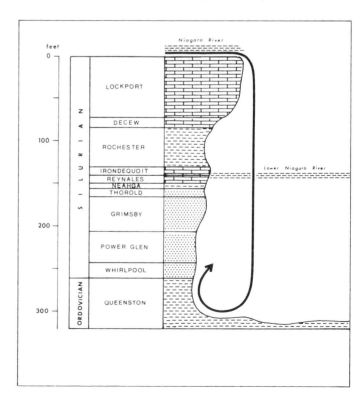

Fig. 8-8   Niagara Falls in relationship to the sedimentary rocks of southern Ontario

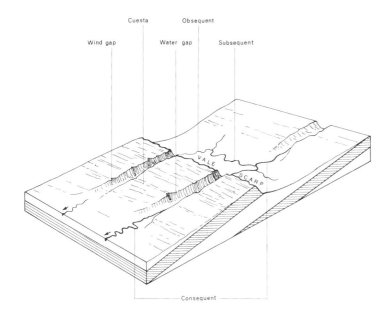

Fig. 8-9 Scarplands and the drainage pattern. A consequent river crosses dipping sedimentary strata and, together with its subsequent tributaries, develops a scarp and vale topography.

Plate 8-3 Thin-bedded dolomites forming part of the Niagara escarpment in the Bruce Peninsula, Ontario. (Geological Survey of Canada, Ottawa.)

now recognized that part of the gorge dates from before the last glaciation and that the postglacial falls only "cleaned out" the till. A buried extension of the upper gorge remains from below the Whirlpool to St. David's. It may have been cut in early Wisconsin time (40,000–50,000 years ago) or in the last interglacial.

Lockport dolomite also forms the cap rock for the Niagara escarpment. This vast east and north-facing cliff appears first in New York State near Rochester, enters Ontario at Queenston, and continues to Hamilton, where it forms the Mountain. At Dundas, the scarp line bends to the north and continues across Ontario to Blue Mountain, overlooking Georgian Bay, the Bruce Peninsula, and Manitoulin Island. The escarpment varies a good deal in character and locally even disappears where it is buried by moraine, particularly in the Orangeville area. In the Niagara Peninsula, it has a maximum height of about 300 feet. The height increases until, in the Blue Mountain sector, the crest is more than 1,800 feet above sea level and 1,000 feet above Georgian Bay. In this area, the escarpment is formed of a vertical cliff in Lockport dolomite; below a ledge is a second minor scarp also in dolomite and, below this, red shales that are often deeply eroded. The face of the scarp is broken at many points by obsequent streams. Some of these are preglacial and are of considerable size, such as the Dundas Valley and the 30-mile-long Beaver Valley. But these are exceptional, and the majority are postglacial in age.

The origin of the Niagara escarpment is associated with the difference in resistance to erosion of the Lockport dolomite and the relatively weak shales that now outcrop to the east of it. In many parts of the world, a structure of this type has led to a scarp and vale topography, with the latter being drained by a major subsequent stream (Fig. 8-9). In southwestern Ontario, although the scarp is present, the vale is either drowned, as in Georgian Bay, or has been modified and buried by glacial deposits. The subsequent river no longer exists in its entirety; in pre-

glacial times, it may have flowed through Georgian Bay and across Ontario from near Collingwood to just west of Toronto. If this was the former course of the river, then the Humber River must mark the southern end of it.

It is not known whether the master consequent streams drained to the southwest towards the centre of the Michigan Basin before flowing to the Mississippi, or whether, as the St. Lawrence does today, it drained to the northeast. Probably, it was to the southwest through the Lake Ontario Basin and the west end of the Niagara Peninsula in a valley now buried in drift.

Southwest of the Niagara escarpment, the bedrock does not often break the surface, and it affects the scenery only indirectly. The rocks in the southwest corner of the province are principally Devonian shales, with local limestones and dolomites. In New York State, dolomitic limestone of the Onondaga (Bois Blanc) Formation produces a prominent scarp that exceeds the Niagara scarp in height. This scarp enters Canada at Fort Erie, but it is not very high and disappears beneath drift near Hagersville. In southwestern Ontario, the bedrock, particularly limestone, occasionally rises close to the surface, and probably in preglacial times it formed low scarps; but it has long since been worn down by ice and covered by drift.

The fundamental elements of the scenery of southern Ontario were in existence by the end of the Tertiary period. The future Great Lakes were broad lowlands, separated by slightly higher ground crossed by scarps that were on the whole more prominent than they are at present. To the northwest, the Canadian Shield had already been exposed from beneath its limestone cover. Less bedrock was visible then than today; for there were long periods of weathering under conditions almost certainly warmer than the present climate which lasted many millions of years, and deep soils covered most of the crystalline rock areas.

The effect of the glaciations on this landscape was extreme. In the earlier discussion

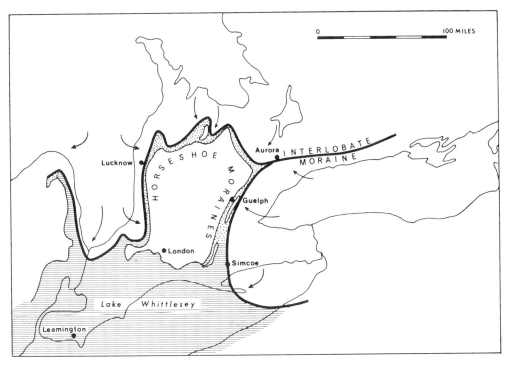

Fig. 8-10   Southern Ontario about 13,000 years ago. The southwestern corner is occupied by glacial Lake Whittlesey, and the only dry land is in the Ontario "island" surrounded by the Horseshoe moraines. (After Chapman and Putnam.)

Plate 8-4   The steep front of the Galt moraine that formed in front of the late Pleistocene ice sheet in southern Ontario.

Plate 8-5   A glacial melt-water channel cut through the Paris moraine : Brantford, Ontario.

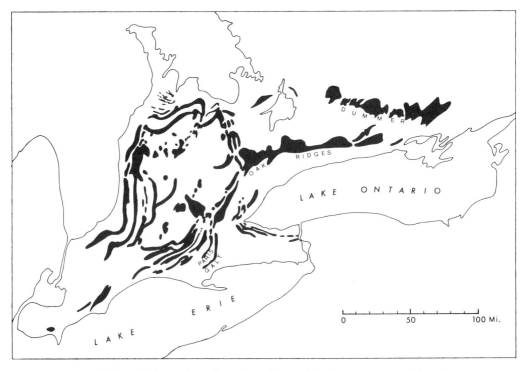

Fig. 8-11   End moraines of southern Ontario (after Chapman and Putnam)

on the Great Lakes, we have already revealed some of the Pleistocene history of southern Ontario, so that now we need only repeat the main ideas with different emphasis. The ice swept over the area on several occasions; and although evidence is lacking, we must assume that in broad outline each glaciation was similar to the one that preceded it. As the ice retreated, it left plains covering large areas. They were quickly modified by melt waters and lakes in some localities, but they are still widely distributed. In detail, they vary considerably; the Dundalk plain, for example, is undulating, ill-drained country with much swamp. In contrast, the Peel till plain north and west of Toronto is in many parts extremely flat, possibly resulting from erosion in a short-lived proglacial lake. The most striking till plains, however, are those which are drumlinized. Drumlins are found in several parts of southern Ontario, but they reach their most spectacular proportions between Lake Scugog and Rice Lake, north of Lake Ontario. In the centre of the drumlin field—and, indeed, built on drumlins—is Peterborough. Other important fields are found south of the Bruce Peninsula.

Towards the close of the glaciation, the glacier ice spread out from the lake basins in all directions, and in the extreme south of Ontario the last ice came from the south and southeast. The effect of this, together with the presence of preglacial uplands, was that two land areas were uncovered early in the ice retreat. The first of these was the high land of southwestern Ontario, which became an island surrounded by ice (Fig. 8-10). Around this island, moraines were deposited which today form the complex, composite ridges of the Horseshoe Moraines. Widely distributed, they reach their maximum in the thick deposits that blanket the Niagara escarpment around Orangeville.

Somewhat later and farther east, ice flowing from the main icecap to the north and east was met by ice moving northwest out of the Lake Ontario basin. It is probable that a moraine had formed along this contact in one of the early glaciations, and that this was strengthened and expanded by later glaciation. By the end of Wisconsin time, a vast, complex interlobate moraine was forming from the vicinity of Trenton to Aurora north of Toronto and westwards to Orangeville, where it joined the Horseshoe Moraines. The Oak Ridges Moraine, as it is known, is over 100 miles long and 7–8 miles wide. It is a hilly, sandy country, often with steep slopes. Once covered with pine and deciduous trees, it was logged over in the early days of settlement, and subsequent soil erosion has led to the creation of sand dunes which are only now being stabilized once more by reforestation.

The last moraines to be deposited in southern Ontario were the Dummer Moraines along the borders of the Shield from the Kawartha Lakes to the east of Tweed (Fig. 8-11). The moraines are rarely more than 10–20 feet high and are extremely bouldery, consisting largely of limestone blocks together with crystalline rocks from the Canadian Shield. The surface is everywhere rough and bouldery, and in places the underlying limestone is exposed, forming bare rock pavements. Elsewhere, drainage is bad and there are many swamps. The Dummer Moraines are the youngest of the landforms produced by ice in southern Ontario and may represent the advance of ice after the Two Creeks interval.

The influence of the proglacial lakes on the landscape has already been mentioned. Locally, wave eroded forms, such as the Iroquois bluff, or the more extensive lacustrine-planed till plains, like the Peel Plain, are important. Of far greater significance are the depositional forms. These include some of the most uniform, and often the most monotonous, physiographic regions of southern Ontario. The lake clay plains are usually flat, although occasionally undulating where morainic ridges break through. The soils are heavy and ill drained; the main areas are the St. Clair Clay Plain, the Haldimand Plain that forms the greater part of the Niagara Peninsula, and the Iroquois Plain along the shores of Lake Ontario. The sand plains, deposited initially in the shallower waters of the lakes,

Plate 8-6   Unconsolidated Pleistocene sediments under erosive attack from gullies and wave action of Lake Ontario. (Information Canada Photothèque. Photo by M. Iger.)

are somewhat more varied. They are often deeply eroded by valleys 50–100 feet deep where they are crossed by rivers entering the lakes. In this group are the large Norfolk Sand Plain, once a soil-denuded area but today a flourishing rural area with prosperous tobacco farms, and the Bothwell Sand Plain, the one-time delta of the Thames River in proglacial Lake Warren.

With the withdrawal of the glacial Great Lakes, southern Ontario already looked very much as we know it today. Aforestation was rapid at the close of the Ice Age, and this had the effect of reducing erosion. But the rivers crossing the lake plains were able to entrench themselves deeply, as did the Humber and the Don, which with their tributaries have produced the system of ravines around Toronto. Waves continued to attack the sand and clay cliffs along the north shores of Lake Erie and Lake Ontario, leading to their retreat and—through the deposition of the eroded material—contributing to the formation of the complex spits of Point Pelee, the Rondeau spit, Long Point, Turkey Point, Burlington Bar, and Toronto Island. At other points, the lacustrine material formed sand dunes, as at Wasaga Beach. With these exceptions, however, changes were small until the nineteenth century, when the population of the region rapidly increased. The subsequent clearing of the land was followed by heavy soil erosion at many points.

Selected Readings

Chapman, L. J., and D. F. Putnam, *The Physiography of Southern Ontario*, Toronto, University of Toronto Press, 1966, 386 pp.

Hobson, G. D., and J. Terasmae, "Pleistocene Geology of the Buried St. David's Gorge, Niagara Falls, Ont., Geophysical and Palynological Studies", *Geol. Surv. Can. Paper* 68-67, 1969.

Karrow, P. F., "Pleistocene Geology of the Scarborough Area", *Ont. Dept. Mines, Geol. Rpt.* No. 46, 1967.

Kumarapeli, P. S., and V. S. Saull, "The St. Lawrence Valley System, A North American Equivalent of the East African Rift Valley System", *Can. Jour. Earth Sciences*, Vol. 3, 1966, pp. 639–658.

McDonald, B.C., *Late Quaternary Stratigraphy and Deglaciation in Eastern Canada* in Turekian, K. K. (ed.), *The Late Cenozoic Glacial Ages*, New Haven, Yale University Press, 1971, pp. 331–353.

Parry, J. T., and J. C. Macpherson, "The St. Faustin – St. Narcisse Moraine and the Champlain Sea", *Rev. Géogr. Montréal*, Vol. 18, 1964, pp. 235–248.

Straw, A., "Late Pleistocene Glacial Erosion Along the Niagara Escarpment of Southern Ontario", *Geol. Soc. Amer. Bull.*, Vol. 79, 1968, pp. 889–910.

9

The Western Interior Plains
(The Prairies)

We have already seen that the Canadian Shield dips along its southern and western margins beneath younger and generally flat-lying sedimentary rocks. On these sedimentary rocks between the rocky uplands of the Shield in the east and the mountains of the Cordillera in the west have developed the Interior Plains. This vast region includes most of the southern Canadian Arctic islands, the Mackenzie Lowlands, the Prairies, as well as the Midwest of the United States, the Great Plains, and the Mississippi Lowland; and on similar rocks between the Shield and the Appalachians are the St. Lawrence Lowlands. In this book, the northern section is discussed as part of the Arctic lands (Chapter 11) and the St. Lawrence Lowlands are also treated separately (Chapter 8); but it must not be forgotten that the physiographic differences between the continental plains in the lower Mackenzie Basin and the western Arctic islands are slight, and that, were it not for the accident of the Canada–United States border, the landscape resemblances between southern Ontario and southern Manitoba would be more evident to Canadians than they are.

The lowlands bordering the Shield are drained by three of the great rivers of the world—the St. Lawrence, the Mississippi, and the Mackenzie. In only two sectors is the dominance of one or other of these rivers missing: in the Arctic, partial drowning by the sea has restricted drainage to relatively minor streams; and in the centre of the continent, there is a zone, corresponding to a large part of the Canadian Prairies, which is committed to neither the Mackenzie nor the Mississippi watersheds, but which is drained by the Saskatchewan River *across* the Canadian Shield to Hudson Bay. It is clear from drift-filled,

former river channels in the Prairies that the drainage was modified during the Quaternary by the glaciations and that, at least for a time, part of the Saskatchewan watershed drained to the Mississippi and the Missouri (Fig. 9-1).

The Interior Plains of western Canada extend more than 1,600 miles from the United States border to the Arctic Ocean. For descriptive purposes, they may be subdivided into the Prairies section in the south (hydrologically corresponding mainly to the Saskatchewan watershed, and the prairie grassland and parkland vegetation belts), the Peace River section in northern Alberta, and the Mackenzie section from Great Slave Lake northwards.

To many visitors, the prairie landscape appears to extend without significant change from the Manitoba–Ontario border to the Rockies. In detail, however, there is considerable variety, and in the next few pages some of these differences will be discussed.

The scenery of the western Canadian plains results from an unusual combination of structural features and glacial modifications. The sediments—mainly clays, shales, and sands—for the most part have so little resisted the geomorphic weathering processes that they rarely outcrop on the surface, but are covered with many tens, and in some cases hundreds, of feet of glacial drift. Where they do appear, it is usually in deep valleys and escarpments. It must not be thought that, because the bedrock is not visible, it has not influenced the development of the landscape; for the major hills, plateaus, and escarpments are located where bedrock is close to the surface. The main river valleys, however, have little relationship to the structure; the river waters come from the melting snows and glaciers

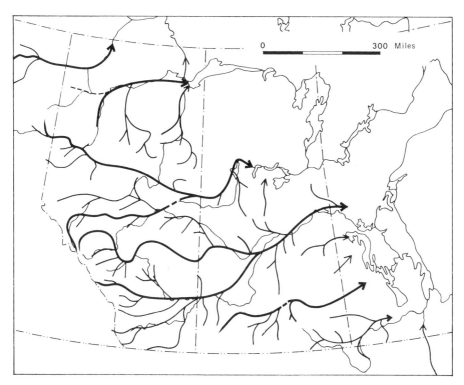

Fig. 9-1   The former river pattern of the Prairies. Note particularly the direction of the early Missouri, which entered Saskatchewan and, joined by the Souris, flowed across southwestern Manitoba. The effect of the glaciations was to divert southwards, either temporarily or permanently, many of the rivers. (Modified after Geological Survey of Canada.)

farther west and flow eastwards in deep valleys, beyond which they have little influence on the evolving scenery of surrounding areas.

The detail of the landscape is a product of the glaciations and particularly of the melt waters in the proglacial lakes and rivers produced at the close of the glaciation. In some places, these waters were responsible for some of the flattest plains in Canada; elsewhere, by contrast, they expanded and deepened channels that are today partly occupied by the rivers. The variations in scenery between different parts of the Prairies therefore result mainly from the dual influences of structure and glaciation. Other regional contrasts in landforms are due to climatic and vegetation differences, especially between the cool and rather moist areas along the northern edges of the Prairies and the arid, often

exceptionally warm regions of the southwest. In the dry zone of southwestern Saskatchewan and southeastern Alberta, vertical slopes characteristic of arid lands, dry valleys, sand dunes, and dust storms are the normal fact of life. Unprotected by a continuous vegetation cover, this land is essentially arid as viewed by the geomorphologist. Very different are the north and east Prairies, whether it be in the grasslands with, under natural conditions, a deep, impenetrable grass sward, or in the forested areas; in both the landscape is basically stable, and is changing slowly.

Underlying the western plains, everywhere, is the Canadian Shield. In Manitoba, the buried surface of the Shield dips to the southwest at a rate of about 6 inches per mile, so that close to the Saskatchewan border it is already below sea level. It continues to sink

Plate 9-1   A dust storm in the southern Prairies: Climax, Sask., May 1959.

westwards, until in Alberta it is more than 2 miles beneath the sedimentary rocks. The surface of the buried Shield is by no means flat, but has been warped into basins and arches which are significant in the location of oil fields; they have no visible effect on the scenery of the southern Prairies, although south of the Alberta–Montana border, the Shield rocks break through the cover rocks to form hills. In Chapter 1, we described how sediments were deposited over the Precambrian basement in the Prairies during the Paleozoic era and again in the late Mesozoic. In the south, the Paleozoic rocks outcrop in Manitoba, where—together with some early Mesozoic formations—they underlie the most easterly of the major physiographic units of the Prairies, known as the Manitoba Lowland or the first prairie level (Fig. 9-2).

Northwest of The Pas, the zone of exposed Paleozoic rocks between the Shield and the Cretaceous rocks narrows and is missing entirely in some places; then, near the border of

the Northwest Territories (60°N), the belt broadens again and roughly half the Mackenzie Lowlands sector has Paleozoic rocks at the surface.

The Manitoba Lowland is 120–150 miles wide between the edge of the Shield and the Cretaceous escarpment in western Manitoba. In the south, it is one of the most prosperous farming areas in Canada, while farther north it becomes a land of marshes, lakes, and forest. The plain has developed primarily on Paleozoic limestones and dolomites, and has been much modified by Pleistocene events. Essentially, it is an extremely level rock plain, broken by low limestone plateaus, of which the most prominent forms the Interlake region between lakes Manitoba and Winnipeg. The Interlake plateau and others farther north are rarely more than 100 feet high and are usually covered with glacial deposits. The sides are often stepped, however, corresponding to resistant rock strata; and here and there, limestone outcrops on the surface. The con-

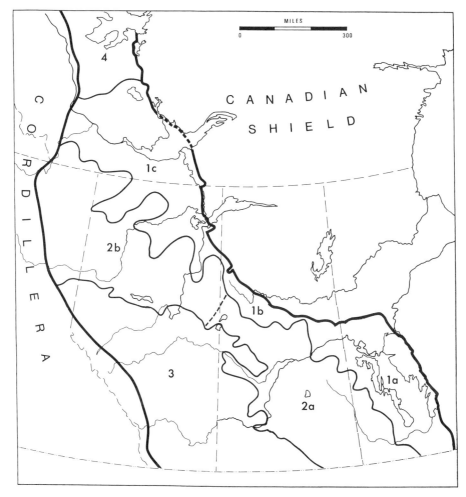

MILES

0   300

CANADIAN SHIELD

C O R D I L E R A

4

1c

2b

3

1b

2a

1a

1	The First Level	2	The Second Level
	a) Manitoba Lowland		a) Saskatchewan Plains
	b) Saskatchewan Lowland		b) Peace Hills and Plains
	c) Slave Lowland		
3	The Third Level		
	Alberta Plains	4	Northern Plains

Fig. 9-2   The Western Plains

tact with the Shield is submerged by Lake Winnipeg, although locally the sandstone beds which form it may be seen on the lake shore. North of The Pas, low dolomite scarps form the Shield contact and resemble closely the scarps of south-central Ontario.

South of the Manitoba Lakes, the bedrock is deeply buried beneath glacial and post-glacial sediments, and exposures of limestone are restricted to isolated mounds, such as Stony Mountain. In the Red River section of the lowland, the silty clays of proglacial Lake Agassiz and the younger alluvial deposits of the river form an unusually flat plain that is notorious for flooding in the spring.

North of a line from Portage La Prairie to Winnipeg, shallow basins in the lowland, probably modified by Laurentide ice and partly blocked by glacial sediments, are occupied by lakes Winnipeg, Winnipegosis, Manitoba, and numerous smaller lakes. Other parts of the lowland, particularly west of Lake

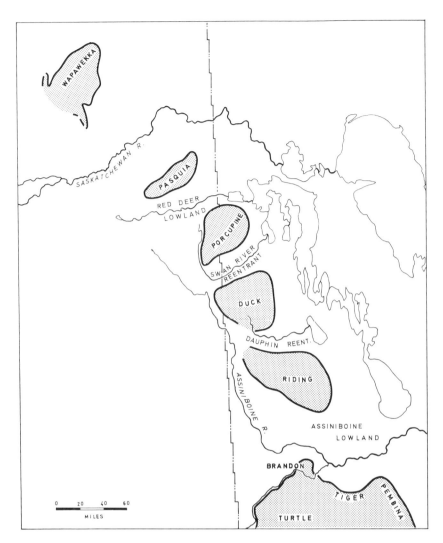

Fig. 9-3   The Manitoba Escarpment and plateaus

Manitoba, are covered with minor moraines, and beaches and sand bars of Lake Agassiz. Elevated glacial-lake beaches are often conspicuous; west of Lake Winnipeg, a prominent beach is named from the town of Gimli, and there are others in the extreme west of the lowland along the base of the Manitoba Escarpment. The largest landform resulting from Lake Agassiz is the proglacial delta of the Assiniboine, which extends from Brandon 35 miles eastwards towards Portage La Prairie. In the western part of the delta, the sands are as much as 150 feet thick. They have been deeply entrenched by streams. The

top of the delta has been blown by the wind to form extensive areas of sand dunes which today are partly fixed by vegetation. East of the steep delta front, fine sands extend as far as Portage La Prairie.

Farther north, the lowland is forested and has extensive areas of muskeg and string bogs. Drainage is poorest where the Saskatchewan River and other streams enter the Manitoba Lakes, producing marshes and numerous deltas. The Carrot River delta, adjacent to the Saskatchewan River, has been drained to provide the most northerly farmland in Manitoba. There are also conspicuous glacial landforms, including a massive end moraine that is followed by the highway south of The Pas.

The corresponding sector of the western plains north of Great Slave Lake has not been described physiographically in detail. In many ways, however, it resembles the northern part of the Manitoba Lowland; it is a complex of rocky plains and low plateaus, often mantled with shattered rock (felsenmeer), undulating drift-covered terrain, and lake and marsh-dotted plains.

As the early European explorers moved westwards from the Red River across the Manitoba Lowland, they saw ahead of them what was apparently a range of hills that separated the first prairie level from a second and higher level to the west. Known today as the Manitoba Escarpment, it forms the eastern margin of the Saskatchewan Plains and the underlying Cretaceous sedimentary rocks, mainly shales, that occupy a great part of the central and western Prairies. In Canada, the Manitoba Escarpment extends for 500 miles from the North Dakota border to the Wapawekka Hills in north-central Saskatchewan; there is a small section in the United States.

At its highest, the escarpment rises more than 1,500 feet above the lowland; at other points, it has been virtually destroyed, where rivers, either today or in the past, crossed it from the west. The escarpment is broken into separate upland units by these valleys (Fig. 9-3). The largest, occupied by the Assiniboine River, is more than 70 miles across, east of Brandon. Farther north, the Dauphin re-entrant between Riding and Duck mountains is no longer occupied by a major through river. Other units, however, are separated by the Swan, Red Deer, and Saskatchewan rivers.

With the exception of the Pembina Hills close to the United States border, the Manitoba Escarpment is separated from the main surface of the Saskatchewan Plains by river valleys. The widest and most continuous of these is occupied by the Assiniboine above Virden, where it flows parallel to the escarpment about 100 miles to the west of it. This course effectively isolates Riding Mountain and Duck Mountain. Similarly, the Swan River Valley separates Porcupine Mountain from the plains to the west.

The character of the face of the escarpment varies considerably along its length (Fig. 9-4), although rarely is a cap rock an

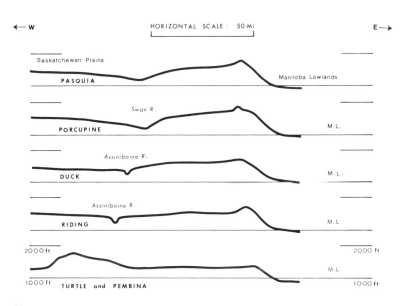

Fig. 9-4   Profiles of the Manitoba Escarpment

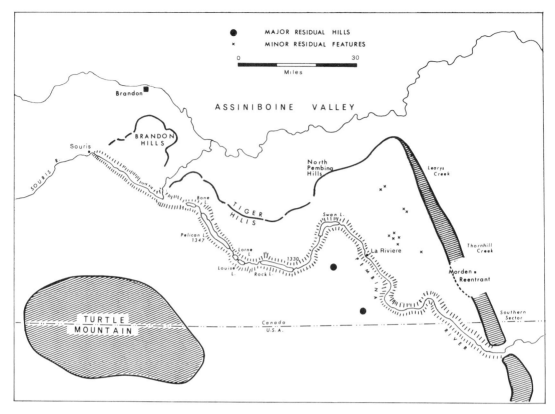

Fig. 9-5   The Pembina escarpment and plateau

important element, as it is in most major sedimentary escarpments in other parts of the world. An exception is in the south, where the siliceous Odanah beds are found in the Riding Mountain shale formation. South of Riding Mountain National Park, the scarp is stepped in many places as a result of beds of varying resistance to erosion in the Upper Cretaceous formations, the action of Lake Agassiz on the lower part of the scarp, and the escape of glacial melt waters around the front of the escarpment. Farther north, although these processes have been locally important, the results are generally obscured by till, glacially thrust bedrock, postglacial ravines, and landslips. Stream activity is conspicuous along Riding Mountain; here, a marked increase in stream erosion in the past 75 years, probably resulting from forest cutting and other disturbances of the ecological balance, is associated with sudden floods that carry down shale fragments which have been spread over the lowland soils below the scarp.

Small landslips have occurred at many points along the escarpment. A large area of jumbled ridges and hollows, which has been described as resulting from massive slumping, covers at least 20 square miles west of Mafeking. Its detailed origin and age are still uncertain.

The Saskatchewan Plains have developed on the Cretaceous shales. The relationship of the Manitoba Escarpment to the plains is most evident south of the Assiniboine, where the scarp of the Pembina Hills, continued westwards as the Pembina Plateau, is separated from the remainder of the Saskatchewan Plains by the open, shallow valley of the Souris River (Fig. 9-5). The surface of the Pembina Plateau is flat, except near the northeast and northern margins, where glacier ice pushed the shale of the scarp edge into low moraine ridges and drumlins. Today these form the Tiger and Brandon hills south of

Carberry and Brandon. Bedrock is rarely far below the plateau surface, and at several places it forms low whaleback ridges, such as Pilot Mound.

The plateau is crossed by a deep channel that was cut by the melt waters of successive Pleistocene ice sheets. The entrance to the channel is near the town of Souris; for the first few miles, it is occupied by the Souris River, but the river then breaks away in a deep valley to the north, flowing past Wawanesa to join the Assiniboine River. The channel continues southeastwards, becoming progressively deeper, until near the United States border it is nearly 500 feet below the upland surface. Streams entering the trough have deposited alluvial fans, which divide it into basins, today occupied by shallow lakes and drained by the Pembina River. The steep, oak-covered slopes and the long narrow lakes that in the summer months attract large pelican colonies make the valley one of the most interesting parts of the southern Prairies.

The Pembina Plateau is unique among the western Manitoba uplands in that it is capped by a low hill. This is Turtle Mountain, and its summit is nearly 2,300 feet above sea level. It is the most easterly outlier of Tertiary sands, sandstones, and lignites, which at one time must have extended without break to the Rocky Mountains, and today form a string of plateaus close to the Canada–United States border. When first seen by Europeans, Turtle Mountain was covered in forest; but much of this has since been cleared from the lower slopes, and on the higher part it has been cut over or burnt and has been replaced by aspen bush. The crest of Turtle Mountain is a maze of lakes, marshes, and low mounds deposited from the last melting ice sheet.

The plateaus north of the Assiniboine–Brandon lowlands have many features in common. The uplands are gently rolling with a glacial drift mantle and numerous shallow lakes; they are crossed, generally from north to south, by valleys that were formed or modified by glacial melt waters, and which have been blocked by later glacial sediments to produce lakes. These features can be seen easily in the aspen woodland of Riding Mountain, particularly in the western part of the National Park where the woods open out to grassland. In contrast, Duck Mountain, Porcupine Mountain, and the plateaus to the northwest are forested, mainly with aspen and birch in the south and spruce in the north.

The Saskatchewan Plains—or, as they are sometimes less appropriately called, the second prairie level—lie in a zone less than 200 miles wide between the Manitoba plateaus and the Missouri Coteau. The scenery results almost entirely from the Pleistocene glaciation. The underlying rock surface is not flat, however, and low domes in the surface on the Cretaceous rocks, combined with morainic debris deposited on them, are the cause of the slightly higher areas of rough terrain that include Moose Mountain, the Touchwood and Beaver hills, the Tiger Hills, and the Allan Hills.

In other sectors, the glaciers left extensive undulating plains of ground moraine, often broken low, sandy ridges, and numerous kettle hollows, where blocks of ice melted and which today are filled with ponds or marshes —the sloughs of the prairie landscape. Elsewhere, there are flat till plains which were frequently washed over briefly by proglacial lakes (Fig. 9-6). The floors of the longer-lived glacial lakes form separate units. Probably the most conspicuous of the latter is the Regina Plain, developed on the clays of glacial Lake Regina, but examples can be found in many other areas. Sandy outwash and glacial lake sands have been blown by the wind into dunes, and extensive areas occur near Saskatoon and downriver near Prince Albert.

The Saskatchewan Plains are crossed by deep, often broad, flat-bottomed valleys. Two large valleys which are combinations of pre-glacial valleys with newer glacial melt water sections are occupied by the north and south branches of the Saskatchewan River. Many of the valleys appear to have been formed as great spillways which drained melt waters from the Pleistocene ice sheet and from the

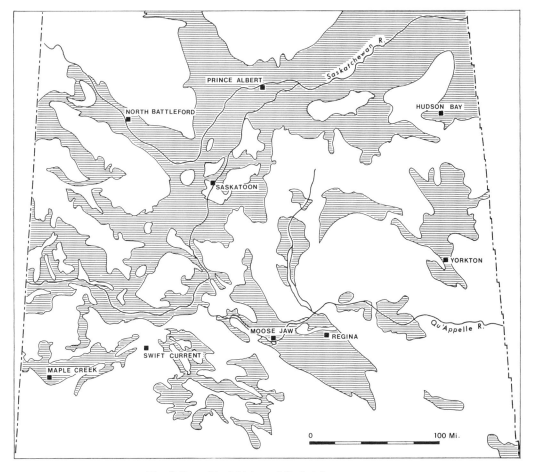

Fig. 9-6   Glacial lakes of Saskatchewan

proglacial lakes to the upper Mississippi at the close of the glaciation. Eight long spillways are found in southern Saskatchewan. Several of these are not more than 20–30 feet deep, but the major spillways—including the Qu'Appelle, the Assiniboine, and the Souris valleys—are locally 200 feet and at one point more than 450 feet deep. Usually they are about a mile wide. The sides are generally steep and landslides are common; in 1956 at Fort Qu'Appelle, following a period of heavy precipitation, a slide about 1,000 feet across occurred.

In southern Saskatchewan east of the Missouri Coteau, almost all the surface run-off is in valleys that were originally spillways or melt-water channels. Locally, preglacial landforms often modified by melt waters and mo-

raines dominate the present landscape, as in Last Mountain Lake northwest of Regina. Farther north, preglacial valleys are more important in controlling the drainage.

The Missouri Coteau marks the boundary between the Saskatchewan Plains and the third prairie level, or Alberta Plains. The Coteau enters Canada from the United States west of Estevan. From there, it may be traced northwestwards as a series of hills—including the Tit, Cactus, and Dirt hills—as far as the south branch of the Saskatchewan River. From the Trans-Canada Highway and the Canadian Pacific Railway near Moose Jaw, the cuesta may be seen extending southeastwards as a line of low hills. Northwest of the Saskatchewan, the Coteau is continued in the Bear Hills; it eventually disappears, buried

Plate 9-2   The Cactus Hills, Sask., part of the Missouri Coteau. The escarpment is strongly gullied at this point.

Plate 9-3   The South Saskatchewan River at the Alberta–Saskatchewan border, deeply incised into the dry plains.

Plate 9-4   The north face of the Cypress Hills, close to the Alberta–Saskatchewan border.

Plate 9-5   Badland topography : Drumheller, Alberta.

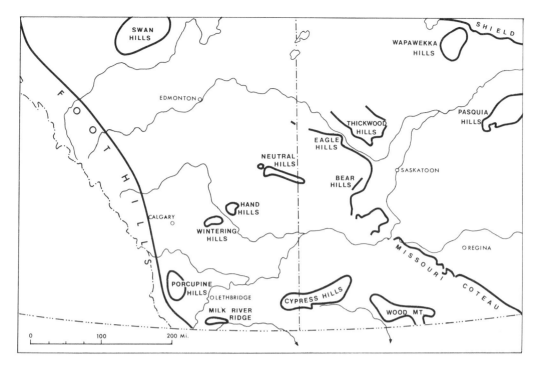

Fig. 9-7   Hills and plateaus of the western Prairie Provinces

beneath glacial deposits in eastern Alberta. The Missouri Coteau is a low, structural escarpment in Upper Cretaceous shales and clays; it resembles, on a smaller scale, the Manitoba Escarpment. The climate of southern Saskatchewan is more arid, however, than the climate along the Manitoba Escarpment. The natural grassland on the Coteau face has failed to protect it from deep ravining, and it is deeply eroded.

In preglacial times the Coteau was probably not more than 200 feet high and had very gentle slopes, except possibly in the most arid parts. The Pleistocene ice sheets advancing across the Saskatchewan Plains thrust into the frozen sediments along the front of the Coteau, forcing them up to greater height than existed before. The Coteau is therefore both an escarpment in its rock structure and a push moraine.

The terrain characteristics of the third prairie level, the Alberta Plains, resemble those of the Saskatchewan Plains. Particularly extensive are areas of rolling parkland that have developed on ground moraine be-

tween Red Deer and Edmonton. Some terrains are more prevalent than farther east— notably the near-desert area of the great Sand Hills south of the South Saskatchewan River and west of Swift Current, which is one of the most arid parts of southern Canada.

Rivers are more deeply entrenched in the Alberta Plains than elsewhere in the Prairies; and, once they leave the foothills zone, many flow considerable distances without receiving major tributaries. The larger rivers, including the Red Deer and both branches of the Saskatchewan, are entrenched several hundreds of feet into Cretaceous shales and sands. So deep are the valleys that in many cases one must reach the brink of their steep sides before one can see the river below. In southern Alberta, rapid postglacial erosion has developed along the banks of the major rivers, producing fascinating badland topography that today is quickly spreading.

Proglacial lakes were generally less important in modifying the landscape in Alberta than farther east. In part, this was because the lakes were more ephemeral, and in southern

Alberta, where the relief is a little greater, the lakes tended to be long and narrow, and occupied river valleys, rather than spreading out as in the eastern Prairies. Glacial melt waters escaped southeastwards into Montana as long as the preglacial drainage to the east was blocked by the retreating ice. The channels known as coulees that were eroded by these melt waters are today often empty of streams. Although formed more than 10,000 years ago, they are still spectacular features; for, under the prevailing arid conditions, the sides have remained nearly vertical, while the floors of the coulees are often occupied by a shallow, usually brackish lake and by saline deposits.

Many residual hills and plateaus lie on the third level of the Alberta Plains (Fig. 9-7). The most conspicuous are the outliers of Tertiary rocks close to the United States border that form Wood Mountain Plateau and

the Cypress Hills. The former is a rolling, treeless upland with numerous abandoned glacial melt-water channels around the margins. The Cypress Hills are more distinctive and extend for nearly 100 miles from east to west. Their survival is due in part to a resistant conglomeritic cap rock that has protected the underlying and weaker sediments from removal. Today, with a surface over 4,500 feet above sea level, the hills form a relatively well-watered outlier of the foothills farther west, and are in sharp contrast to the surrounding short-grass prairie and sagebrush country of southeastern Alberta and southwestern Saskatchewan. The gently rolling upper surface of the hills is deeply entrenched by valleys which contain streams of clear water and whose slopes are clothed with coniferous woods.

In Alberta, the Border Plateau, the Wintering Hills, the Hand Hills, the Neutral Hills,

Plate 9-6   Gullies and valley sides of the Oldman River encroach into the surface of the western prairie : near Lethbridge, Alberta. (Information Canada Photothèque. Photo by G. Hunter.)

Plate 9-7   The Neutral Hills, south-central Alberta.

and the Porcupine Hills close to the Rocky Mountains in some cases are other Tertiary outliers; and some originated as push moraines thrust up by the Pleistocene ice sheet where it met slightly higher ground.

Finally, in the west as the Rockies are approached, the plains rise more quickly. Here, the sediments have undergone faulting, which marks the outermost fringe of the great contortions experienced in the Rocky Mountain Front along the length of Alberta. It is a rolling, often hilly country, crossed by the deep valleys of streams originating in the Rockies. The foothills, with their black soils, substantial precipitation, and streams, are one of the richer areas of western Canada; and the magnificent backdrop formed by the snow-covered peaks of the Rockies adds to their attraction.

Selected Readings

Edmunds, F. H., "Recession of Wisconsinan Glacier from Central Saskatchewan", *Sask. Dept. Mineral Resources Rept.* 67, 1967, 23 pp.

Farvolden, R. N., "Bedrock Channels of Southern Alberta," *Res. Council of Alberta, Bull.*, No. 12, 1963, pp. 63–75.

Gravenor, C. P., and L. A. Bayrock, *Glacial Deposits of Alberta* in Legget, R. F., *Soils in Canada*, Toronto, University of Toronto Press, 1961, pp. 33–50.

Kupsch, W. O., "Ice Thrust Ridges in Western Canada", *Jour. Geol.*, Vol. 70, 1962, pp. 582–594.

Westgate, J. A., *The Quaternary Geology of the Edmonton Area, Alta.* in Pawluk, S. (ed.), *Pedology and Quaternary Research*, Edmonton, University of Alberta Press, 1969, pp. 129–151.

10

The Canadian Shield

The Canadian Shield is the geological nucleus of Canada and, indeed, of the whole North American continent. This vast, roughly circular area of Precambrian rocks occupies most of eastern and central Canada, and on the south side projects into the states of New York, Michigan, Wisconsin, and Minnesota. The rocks of the Shield are largely the end product of mountain-building episodes in Precambrian times; in the 500 million years since that time, there have been no further orogenies in the Shield, and tectonic activity has been intermittent and for long periods limited to uplift of broad crustal areas.

The exposed surface of the Canadian Shield extends for nearly 2,500 miles from north to south and not much less from east to west (Fig. 10-1). The Shield is, in fact, far larger; buried beneath younger sediments, it extends to the Western Cordillera and southeastwards to the Appalachian–Acadian belt of folded rocks. At several points in the United States, in Oklahoma and in Montana, the Shield projects through the rocks of the Interior Plains and produces isolated mountains and uplands. In addition, most of Greenland is part of the same Precambrian continental nucleus.

The Canadian Shield is one of several shields that form the nuclei of the continents. It is the largest of the extra-tropical shields, and in its geomorphological evolution resembles closely the Fennoscandian Shield; in contrast, the tropical and subtropical shields, although sharing with the Canadian Shield some major elements in geological development, differ greatly in detail of the landscape. An explanation of these differences is an intriguing problem for future research.

For most Canadians, the image of the Shield is a forest-covered terrain of rock knobs and hills as typified by its southern margin from near Quebec City in the east, to the Laurentians north of Montreal and Ottawa, through central Ontario and around the north shore of Lake Superior, to Lake of the Woods in eastern Manitoba. Along this belt, crossed today by the Trans-Canada Highway and by the Canadian Pacific transcontinental railway, the scenery is uniform for great distances; and the traveller may be forgiven for thinking that it is characteristic of the whole Shield. It is true that this terrain is repeated many times as the Shield is crossed towards the Arctic, with only the vegetation changing from closed boreal forest to subarctic woodlands, and eventually in the far north to tundra—a land that is monotonous, often sterile, and, beyond the limit of commercial forest, valuable only for the mineral wealth it contains and the water that flows over it. Actually, even within the southern belt, the differences of the scenery are considerable, and a visit to other parts of the Shield shows that the scenery has much variety. But the uniform response of the dominant gneissic rocks to the geomorphic processes does lead to great monotony in the landscape.

The fact remains that only a small sector of the Canadian Shield is known to many Canadians. It has a hostile environment for most of man's activities, and the population and transportation routes are generally restricted to the southern perimeter. The inner zone, apart from a few exceptions where mining communities have developed, is still an unsettled, unproductive, unknown land.

The scientific analysis of the scenery of the Canadian Shield has barely commenced. The reasons for this are largely historical, for

Fig. 10-1   The Canadian Shield : exposed and bordering buried sector

much of the description of Canadian physiography has been, directly or by implication, a projection of earlier studies in the United States. These were developed without reference to Shield areas and have not proved particularly suitable for them. Physiographic description of tropical shields has been more successful. L. C. King, first in Africa (1963) and then in other parts of the tropical world (1967), has developed a model of practical value. Unfortunately, attempts to apply it to mid-latitude shields have not been so useful.

The first comprehensive and rational description of the Canadian Shield was by Bos-

tock (1964, and modified 1969). His basic (and largest) units, however, are structural regions of the Shield as proposed by Stockwell (1963), and it remains to be seen how practical it will be to describe contemporary landscapes in terms of geological events that ceased between 1,000 and 2,500 million years ago.

We have already seen (Chapter 1) that the Shield experienced several mountain-building episodes in Precambrian time. Before the end of the Proterozoic era, the mountains had been reduced by erosion to plains and hills of moderate relief (Fig. 10-2). Possibly, by this

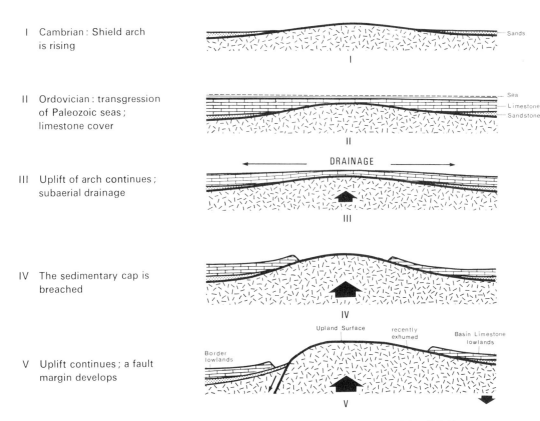

I Cambrian: Shield arch is rising

II Ordovician: transgression of Paleozoic seas; limestone cover

III Uplift of arch continues; subaerial drainage

IV The sedimentary cap is breached

V Uplift continues; a fault margin develops

Fig. 10-2   Evolution of the margin of the Shield

time the Shield had developed an undulating surface, with arches and domes of higher land separating shallow basins several hundreds of miles across. Certainly, the wave-form was present in the Paleozoic era and may have continued developing in later geological times. A partial and a very tentative reconstruction of the basin and swell form is shown in Fig. 10-3.

In the late Ordovician period, a shallow sea spread over much, and perhaps all, of the Canadian Shield. In it were deposited limestones and dolomites which ultimately buried the former land surface. The sea had withdrawn by Early Silurian time; and although it expanded again later, it failed to cover as much land as did its predecessor. Whether the whole Shield was buried by the Ordovician limestone is not known, but the scattered outcrops that have survived until the present make it appear most probable (Fig. 10-4).

As the Paleozoic sea withdrew, the limestone plains covering the Shield were exposed to denudation. The limestone was removed first from the highest parts, corresponding to the arches and domes, to expose the sub-Paleozoic Shield land surface. These areas appear to have been denuded slowly and uniformly throughout the Mesozoic and Cenozoic eras, and for much of the time may have had a deeply weathered mantle. Partial confirmation of this view comes from central Quebec–Labrador, where Cretaceous fossil wood has been found. The flat upland plains which originated in this way, including the plains around Contwoyto Lake in the western Arctic and the lake plateau of Labrador–Quebec, are uniformly of low relief and are generally 1,500–2,000 feet above sea level. They have the appearance of extensive, elevated peneplains, and the term is widely used —for example, "the Laurentian peneplain" —but it is doubtful whether they are in the

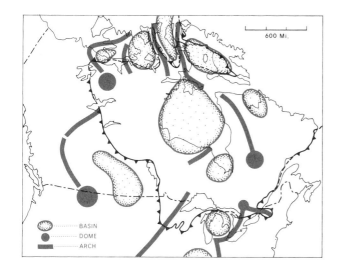

Fig. 10-3   Hypothetical basins and arches of the exposed Canadian Shield and its buried margins

last stage of a Davisian cycle of erosion.

On the basis of its evolution, Shield scenery may be classified into a few dominant types that are largely independent of the underlying rock. First are the flat-topped uplands on the crest of the domes and arches; they are normally distant from the sea and escaped intense denudation during the accelerated uplift that occurred in other sectors in the Cenozoic era. These areas may locally have relief of several hundreds of feet with short, steep-sided valleys and lake basins; but in general, they are poorly drained by major rivers flowing in wide, shallow valleys.

The outer side of the arch towards the margin of the Shield takes several forms. Where the slope is gentle and unbroken by faulting, the Shield surface disappears beneath the younger sedimentary rocks, as occurs in Manitoba and south-central Ontario. The terrain is flat, with low rocky knobs rising not more than a few tens of feet above the lakes and valleys. Where the margin of the Shield is more abrupt, and often associated with faulting, the perimeter zone is deeply dissected, hilly, and in places mountainous.

On the inner side of the arches, the Shield surface was exposed (exhumed) from beneath the limestones during the Tertiary and Early Quaternary periods, and the morphology is very little different from the Early Paleozoic land surface as it was before the Ordovician seas. Today the terrain is flat and is crossed by rivers, either in shallow valleys, or in many cases in no valleys at all. Finally, on the inner side, the Shield passes beneath an escarpment marking the edge of the sedimentary rocks which continue to fill the innermost part of the basins.

When examined in detail, the drainage of the Shield is complex; but in its major outline, it follows closely the regional contours of the Shield. In general, it appears to have developed on the limestone cover which had the same basin and dome form as the underlying Shield; as the sedimentary rocks were denuded, the drainage was superimposed onto the Shield. Subsequently, the pattern has been deranged by glaciation, by faulting (especially with the formation of graben, such as Bathurst Inlet, N.W.T., and the Lake St. John Lowland), and by the superimposition of streams onto a Shield surface that sloped in a different direction. This appears to have been the case west of Hudson Bay, where the major rivers flow to the east and are believed to have been superposed from the limestone; all the tributaries flow north and represent the slope of the Shield in this direction.

The outer circumference of the Shield is more than 7,000 miles, and in this great distance there is considerable variety. Most striking are the highlands in the northeast

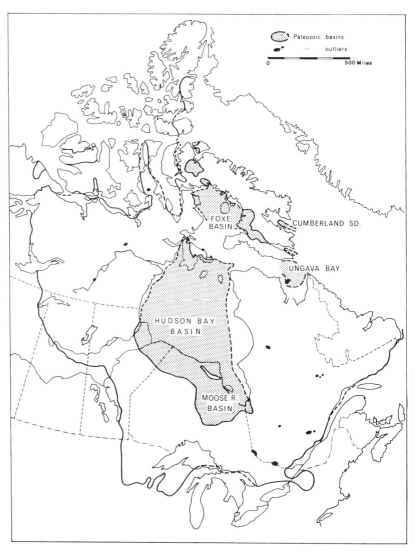

Fig. 10-4   Paleozoic outcrops on the Canadian Shield: the surviving remnants
of formerly more extensive Paleozoic limestones and dolomites. Distribution on
the sea floor is inferred from seismic observation.

sector; here, from southern Ellesmere and Devon islands in the Queen Elizabeth Islands, to Bylot and Baffin islands and Labrador, is some of the most spectacular scenery in Canada. A stark coast rises almost vertically out of the sea to uplands at 5,000 and 6,000 feet that are partly covered with glaciers and deeply dissected by steep-sided fiords. It is one of the finest fiord coasts in the world. This highland rim is not strictly the edge of the Shield, because an arch may have extended across Baffin Bay to connect with the Greenland Shield. Early in the Tertiary period, the crest of the arch collapsed, probably in association with continental drift, leaving the high sides of Baffin Island and west Greenland, and, between the two, a depressed basin now occupied by Baffin Bay, Davis Strait, and the Labrador Sea. Short, fast-flowing rivers eroded deep valleys on both the Canadian and Greenland coasts; and then, during the Pleistocene glaciations, these valleys were occupied by great outlet glaciers which modified them to fiords.

The southern margin of the Shield is generally lower than the eastern, although in most places it is still a major topographic barrier. This is particularly true along the north shore of the gulf and estuary of the St. Lawrence between the Strait of Belle Isle and Quebec City, where the Shield rises precipitously 1,500–3,000 feet either directly from the water, as between Quebec and Tadoussac, or a few miles inland at the rear of a narrow coastal plain, as it does near Seven Islands. In much of this sector, the edge of the Shield is a fault-line scarp of complex origin. The escarpment westwards from Quebec to Ottawa—where, as the Gatineau Hills, it overlooks the federal capital—also has a fault origin. The Precambrian Shield rocks have been down-faulted on the St. Lawrence side and are buried by young rocks 1,000 feet or more beneath the lowland surface. At a few points, notably in the Two Mountains area between Montreal and Ottawa, the Shield breaks through the sediments to form "islands" of Precambrian rock in the Paleozoic lowlands. For nearly a thousand miles from the Strait of Belle Isle to Ottawa, the edge of the Shield is broken by deep valleys—in some places, great gorges, where the rivers break out from the interior to the coast. It is along these valleys that entry is possible to the interior uplands of the Shield; and they are followed by the Quebec, Labrador, and North Shore Railway into New Quebec and by the highways north from Ottawa, Montreal, and Three Rivers.

Between Ottawa and Sault Ste. Marie, the edge of the Shield dips gently beneath the younger sedimentary rocks. The boundary of the Shield is an uneven line. In some parts, the Precambrian rocks project into the adjacent lowlands, while in other localities low Paleozoic limestone plateaus are preserved on the Shield. The sequence of scenery is clear in Ontario if one travels westwards between Brockville and Kingston: the limestone plains of eastern Ontario are replaced by the Shield at the Frontenac Axis, visible as the Thousand Islands in the St. Lawrence, only to be buried beneath limestone plateaus beyond the axis

between Gananoque and Kingston. In these areas, the Shield is not deeply dissected, and the difference in elevation with the lowlands is not nearly as great. Instead, there are flat rock plains, such as those west of the Rideau Lakes, north of the Kawartha Lakes, and east of Georgian Bay; occasionally, the relief is greater and there are low hills, as in the Muskoka region. The whole of this area is an exhumed zone from which the Paleozoic rocks have been removed in recent geological time. The edge of the retreating sedimentary rocks commonly produces low scarps facing the Shield. Although not high, they are often prominent, as on northern Manitoulin Island; or north of Lindsay, Ontario, where the Kawartha Lakes are trapped between limestone scarps and the Shield.

Westwards again, the edge of the Shield in Canada is higher and forms picturesque scenery along the north shore of Lake Superior. We must remember, however, that this is not strictly the margin of the Shield; for it continues southwards in Minnesota and Wisconsin, and the steep north shore of Lake Superior is in fact *within*, rather than on the edge of, the Shield. In Canada, the true margin of the Shield does not reappear until west of Lake of the Woods. From the Manitoba–Minnesota border to Great Slave Lake, the Shield generally rises from beneath younger rocks; the relief is rarely great, and the contact is often buried beneath glacial deposits. This is especially true near the Slave (Mackenzie) River, north of The Pas (Manitoba), and in southeastern Manitoba along the Trans-Canada Highway. Elsewhere in the west, low scarps, normally of Paleozoic limestone, overlap onto the Shield; and lakes, including Lake Winnipeg, have developed along the contact.

For a distance of less than 300 miles between Great Slave and Great Bear lakes, the edge of the Shield is again high and backed by rugged hill country. But in general, the west and southwest sides of the Shield are relatively low in contrast to the high—and in the northeast, extremely high—margins of eastern Canada.

The scenery of the northern, Arctic boundary of the Shield is very different. Unlike the long, linear stretches of the Shield edge in the south, several fingers of Precambrian rocks penetrate northwards from the continental mainland onto the Arctic islands. These areas include a belt of rocks in western Victoria Island; the Wellington Arch in south-central Victoria; the Boothia–Somerset Arch, which effectively divides the east and the west Arctic; and in the east, the Melville Arch. Scenically, the northern margin of the Shield is extremely variable, with sectors of flat, recently exhumed surfaces (for example, south of Queen Maud Gulf), and high hills and escarpments, where faulting or steeply dipping surfaces mark the edge of the Shield, as on the west side of the Boothia Arch.

Although the major surface elements of the Shield may be interpreted in terms of a warped, very ancient land surface, other causes have been operative in moulding the landscape. It has already been shown how significant faulting has been in defining the perimeter of the Shield. Faulting within the Shield has also been important. Since most of the faults are of great geological age, their effect on the landscape is today of a secondary nature and results from differential weathering, where contrasting rocks have been brought into contact by faulting. Where there are two parallel faults and the crust between drops to form a graben, the resulting landforms—even when modified by later erosion —produce striking features. In the Canadian Shield, there are many examples—Frobisher Bay (N.W.T.), Hamilton Inlet (Labrador), the St. John Lowland (Quebec), the Ottawa Valley above Ottawa, Wager Bay (N.W.T.), and Bathurst Inlet (N.W.T.), to name some of the largest.

Minor faults and regional joint patterns imprint strong *linear* patterns on many of the Shield rocks, and these are revealed in the landscape today as long straight valleys, fiord walls, lake sides, and scarps.

It has been shown in Chapter 1 that predominantly gneissic granitic rocks comprise more than 80 per cent of the surface of the Shield. Although these rocks were formed over a vast interval of time, perhaps in excess of 3,000 million years, their chemical composition is remarkably constant and their response to geomorphic processes is exceptionally uniform. The reputed monotony of the Shield scenery must be explained by this constancy of rock type, as there is no apparent difference, at least on a significant and visible scale, in granitic scenery wherever the relief is the same, anywhere in the Shield.[1] Characteristically, where the relief is moderate (50– 500 feet), there are low hills with steep basal slopes and convex, usually bare rock upper slopes—the scenery familiar to many Canadians in the Laurentians or with lesser relief in the Muskoka district, in the rock knobs of eastern Manitoba, or in the hills around Yellowknife.

The basic characteristic in Canadian granitic scenery is the presence of linear features resulting from regional joint and fracture systems in the rocks which are parallel and commonly orthogonal over broad areas. Where denudational energy is low (for example, in recently exhumed areas in basins or on the crest of arches), the structural pattern may be visible only in the drainage; however, where denudation has been powerful, as on the sides of arches or near major faults, the surface is incised along the linears. Consequently, the terrain is broken into blocks, the height of which is controlled by the local base level and the dimensions of the structural pattern. Several geomorphic agents have been proposed to explain the incision. Stream erosion is the most obvious cause, although it is often difficult to show in detail how the drainage pattern developed, unless there has been repeated and complex stream capture. An alternative suggestion has been that encroaching permafrost in the Early Pleistocene epoch

---

[1] The absence of major differences in landforms developed on granitic rocks through more than 25° of latitude and between climates varying from the mid-latitude east continental type of southern Ontario and the arid, high Arctic type of Somerset Island suggests strongly that morphological analysis based principally on climatic regions has only limited value.

Plate 10-1   Contorted granite-gneiss of Precambrian age from northern Quebec. This rock is characteristic of large areas of the Canadian Shield. (Geological Survey of Canada, Ottawa.)

shattered and widened moisture-rich fracture zones, and that glacier ice subsequently removed the debris. An attractive third hypothesis postulates a long period of stable climatic, vegetation, and tectonic conditions in the Tertiary period, when the climate was warm and humid. Under these conditions, deep weathered mantles would form, certainly many tens of feet thick and—if contemporary tropical conditions are analogous—hundreds of feet thick in joint and fracture zones. Subsequently, the convulsion of Pleistocene time led to the removal of the weathered material by streams and ice, and minor surface modifications that followed resulted in the present scenery.

Within the granitic rocks are small enclaves of metamorphosed volcanic and sedimentary rocks. Larger areas of folded and deformed volcanic and sedimentary rocks form the Grenville Province in the southeast of the Shield in Ontario and Quebec; others occur in the Labrador Trough. Although rocks of very different geological ages are present in this group, denudation has produced similar types of scenery, mainly ridges and valleys— some straight, some curved and varying considerably in scale.

In the Labrador Trough, which extends from near the source of the Hamilton River to the west side of Ungava Bay, the parallel ridges on resistant slates and quartzites, and the valleys in dolomites resemble Appalachian ridge and valley topography. Comparable scenery is found in the Povungnituk Hills between Cape Smith and Wakeham Bay in extreme northern Quebec. In other areas, the folding has been more intense; but although they are often greatly contorted, the sediments have not lost their identity. Under these conditions, the folds appear in the scenery as parallel and sub-parallel curving ridges. They are particularly prominent west of Roes Welcome Sound, in the Belcher Islands, and on the southeast side of Great Slave Lake.

Contrasting with the types of Shield scenery already described are the plains developed on flat-lying to gently dipping Proterozoic sandstones, limestones, and dolomites. Small areas of these rocks occur in the southern Shield; but the largest are in the northwest, where they underlie the middle Thelon Basin and the plains southeast of Lake Athabasca. Volcanic rocks are often associated with these sediments. Thick basalt flows form magnificent cuesta scenery in the Coronation Gulf area, including Bathurst Inlet, in the western Arctic. Elsewhere, diabase sills were intruded into late Precambrian sediments; and where these are exposed, they produce high, dark, vertically fluted cliffs. The most accessible scenery of this type is around Thunder Bay at the head of Lake Superior; other fine examples exist in the Shaler Mountains of northern Victoria Island.

This analysis has shown that the major elements of the Shield landscape have arisen from the modification by tectonic forces of an ancient surface that may date from Late Precambrian or Early Paleozoic times. Today no part of this surface is visible, except where it has been exposed by the removal of later rocks. Local relief at the present time is a direct result of the energy available in the different parts of the Shield after changes in level of this surface. The minor bedrock landforms result from the variable response of the different rocks to the denudation processes; consequently, much of the variety in Shield scenery arises from variations in the 20 per cent of the rocks that are not of deep igneous origin.

Finally, a third set of scenic modifications is associated with the Quaternary history of the Shield. The effect of the postglacial marine transgression on the limestone lowlands has already been noted, and the same process affected wide areas of the exhumed plains west of Hudson Bay, southeast of James Bay, and south of Queen Maud Gulf. The glaciations also produced many modifications in the preglacial landscape. Undoubtedly, the most striking of these is in the highland rim of the northeast, where outlet glaciers from the continental ice sheet escaped to the Labrador Sea and Davis Strait, modifying the deep valleys into fiords. Elsewhere, the erosive effect of the ice was less spectacular, but there is much evidence of abrasion and smoothing by ice. It is not always correct, however, to suggest that the present barren rock topography of the Shield margins is entirely a product of glacial erosion; more accurately, it could be described as being due to glacial removal of what were really preglacial, deep-weathered mantles. In fact, many of the lakes so common in many parts of the Shield come rather from the damming of preglacial valleys, often formed along linears, than from overdeepening in any preferred direction by the ice.

Deposition from the Pleistocene ice sheets has greatly modified many Shield landscapes. The extent of the large drumlins and drumlinoid fields has been described briefly in the chapter on glaciation; and it must not be overlooked that west of Hudson Bay, particularly in the Thelon Plain, are some of the largest drumlin fields in the world. In other areas, fluvioglacial landforms rather than till features are prominent, particularly in the esker zones of the Northwest Territories and northern Quebec. Elsewhere, sediments were deposited from the ice sheet directly into proglacial lakes and were never moulded into conspicuous landforms. Frequently, glacial till, outwash, and lacustrine deposits in combination bury the Shield rocks; and the rugged, soil-free, rock knob hills of the southern

Shield are often replaced in the interior of the Shield by wide depositional plains that are broken only by occasional rock outcrops. Nowhere is this modification more important than in the Clay Belt of northeastern Ontario and northwestern Quebec.

Selected Readings

Ambrose, J. W., "Exhumed Paleoplains of the Precambrian Shield of North America", *Am. Jour. Sci.*, Vol. 262, 1964, pp. 817–857.

Hare, F. K., "Photo Reconnaissance Survey of Labrador–Ungava", *Geog. Branch Mem.* 6, 1959, 83 pp.

King, L. C., *The Morphology of the Earth*, Edinburgh, Oliver and Boyd, 1967, 726 pp.

Stockwell, C. H., "Tectonic Map of the Canadian Shield", *Geol. Surv. Can. Map* 4, 1965.
    et al., *Geology of the Canadian Shield* in Douglas, R. J. W. (ed.), *Geology and Economic Minerals of Canada*, Ottawa, Queen's Printer, 1971, pp. 44–150.

11

The Arctic Lands

Arctic Canada covers 1.2 million square miles or nearly a third of the whole of Canada. More than half the ice-free Arctic lands of the northern hemisphere are within the Canada realm, and the area of glaciers is second only to that of Greenland. The Canadian Arctic is 2,500 miles across from northern Yukon to Labrador, and nearly 1,800 miles from Cape Columbia in northern Ellesmere land to James Bay. By any measure, the Arctic is a vast land. Its scenery is probably the most distinctive, and certainly the least known, of all of Canada.

In part of the Quaternary, the Arctic was even more extensive than it is today. At the height of the Ice Ages, a zone of the arctic terrain surrounded the outer margin of the ice sheets to a width of several hundred miles in Europe, and to a somewhat narrower extent in North America. As the ice front retreated at the close of the last glaciation, the tundra zone moved northwards and finally occupied its present position. For a brief period, at one time or another in the last 12,000 years, all parts of Canada must have experienced arctic conditions.

There are many possible definitions of the Arctic. The biggest environmental changes between the polar and mid-latitude lands occur close to the treeline, and for most practical purposes the terrestrial Arctic may be defined as the treeless terrains beyond the northern forests. This definition produces difficulties, as there may be a broad sector more than 100 miles wide of tundra-forest, in which patches of tundra and woods are intermingled, rather than a clearly defined treeline. For the purpose of this chapter, however, the treeline extending from the Mackenzie delta, diagonally southeastwards to Churchill, and then following closely the southwest side of Hudson Bay defines the Arctic northwest of James Bay (Fig. 11-1). In Quebec, the treeline extends from north

TABLE 12-1
CIRCUMPOLAR ENVIRONMENTAL
ZONES (square miles)

	Arctic		Northern Subarctic
	Glacier-covered	Ice-free	Forest-tundra and open woodland
Alaska	25	210,000	210,000
Canada	60,000	1,140,000	570,000
Greenland	730,000	110,000	—
Iceland	4,700	36,000	—
N. Atlantic Islands	22,500	1,900	—
Scandinavia	35	7,000	42,000
U.S.S.R.	24,000	770,000	2,000,000

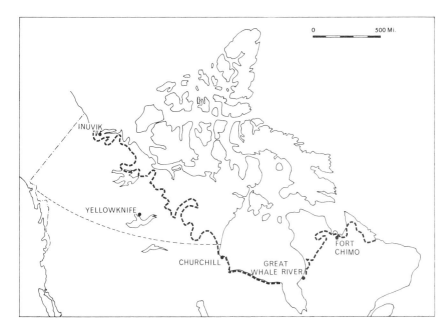

Fig. 11-1   The tree-line in Canada

of Great Whale River to Ungava Bay and across to the Labrador coast.

North of the treeline, there are no continuous areas of trees, although there may be isolated clumps of spruce; the ground is everywhere permanently frozen, and ice is an important agent in many geomorphic processes. It is hardly surprising that, in a region as large as the Canadian Arctic, there are major differences of environment and landscape. The scenery varies from the flat, prairie-like lowlands of interior Keewatin, to the spectacular, ice-covered mountains overlooking the fiords of Baffin Island; and in the very far north, the arid desert landscapes of the mountains of Axel Heiberg and Ellesmere islands. In spite of major regional differences, there are certain basic elements that are repeated everywhere. In all parts of the Arctic, moisture—whether it is in the air, on the ground, or deep within the soil—is frozen annually for many months and often for the whole of the year. On the surface, the vegetation is extremely variable in the protection it provides the ground; while in some areas there is a dense, closed plant cover, in many localities the vegetation is discontinuous and

the soils are exposed to strong geomorphic action. The density of the plant cover and the number of species decreases from south to north. In the northern islands of the Queen Elizabeth Archipelago, aridity, low temperatures, and the brief summer restrict closed plant associations to the damper, protected valleys. On the islands south of Parry Channel, deserts are less extensive and are concentrated on the uplands or shattered-rock lowlands; where surface moisture is available to plants, particularly in the western Arctic, closed tundra communities are common. On the mainland, closed plant covers predominate, although they may vary from wet, marsh, and hillock tundras to heath and dwarf bush tundra in the drier parts. Close to the treeline, willows and arctic birch, which are found in sheltered positions throughout the Arctic, become numerous; and in favoured localities, where there is natural irrigation, small woods of these bushes are common.

Today only 5 per cent of the Canadian Arctic is covered by glaciers. With few exceptions, the glaciers are located on the highland northeastern rim overlooking the Labrador Sea, Baffin Bay, and Kane Basin, where

Plate 11-1   A model of mountainous topography on Axel Heiberg Island, with valley glaciers flowing off the highlands towards the main moraine and outwash-filled valley. (Model: National Research Council. Photo: Geological Survey of Canada, Ottawa.)

a combination of altitudes in excess of 5,000 feet and moisture from partly open seas favour glacier development. On the mainland, permanent ice is limited to a few cirque-and-valley glaciers in northern Labrador. These have dwindled rapidly during the climatic amelioration of the present century. North of Hudson Strait, the ice is more extensive. The most southerly icecaps are found on the uplands on both sides of Frobisher Bay; and north of Cumberland Sound, ice almost buries the Penny Highlands. With the exception of the Barnes Icecap, all the Baffin Island glaciers are close to the fiords that penetrate the eastern coast of the island. The Barnes Icecap is located in the centre of the island on a rolling, upland surface, and is significantly lower than other large ice fields. It has been suggested that it may be a relic of a Pleistocene ice sheet.

North of Parry Channel, nearly all the highlands of east Devon, eastern and northern Ellesmere, and Axel Heiberg islands are ice-covered. Two other areas of permanent ice should be noted: there are small glaciers on Melville Island, in the western part of the Queen Elizabeth Archipelago; and glaciers exist on the mountain ranges of the Alaska–Yukon border and the interior Yukon. The latter are generally referred to as alpine rather than arctic.

Four major structural regions are found in the Arctic: the Canadian Shield primarily exposed on the mainland, but projecting northwards into the archipelago at several places; the Paleozoic sedimentary rock province of the south-central and southwestern islands that mantles the north and northwest of the Shield; the Innuitian Province of the Queen Elizabeth Islands; and the Arctic coastal plain, close to the shores of the Arctic Ocean. This structural classification does not

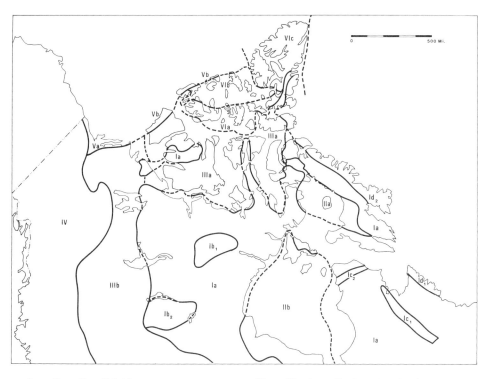

I	Canadian Shield	III	Northern Platform Lowlands	
	a) Lowlands, hills, and plateaus		a) Arctic islands	
	b) Sandstone plains		b) Mackenzie Lowlands	
	c) Folded sedimentary hills	IV	Cordillera	
	d) Highland rim	V	Arctic Coastal Plain	
II	Interior Lowlands	VI	Innuitian Province	
	a) Foxe Basin		a) Parry Hills	
	b) Hudson Bay Basin		b) Sverdrup Plain	
			c) Northern mountains	

Fig. 11-2   The physiographic regions of northern Canada

provide an adequate basis for physiographic description; therefore, a modification of it is presented in Fig. 11-2.

An interpretation of the Shield topography in terms of basins and arches has already been made (Chapter 10). It explains the major landform elements of the Arctic Shield and the position of the associated limestone lowlands that form region II in the southern islands of the archipelago. North of Parry Channel, the major landform units have developed in response to the main geological divisions of the folded Parry rocks, the sediments of the Sverdrup Basin and the Arctic coast, and the exposed folded rocks north of

the basin in Ellesmere and Axel Heiberg islands.

It must be assumed that the northern extremity of the continent was at one time a single land mass that was broken up to form the Arctic Archipelago through a combination of faulting and river erosion. The broad through channel—the true Northwest Passage —known in various parts as M'Clure Strait, Viscount Melville Sound, Barrow Strait, and Lancaster Sound, and collectively as Parry Channel, is probably fault-controlled. The coasts of many of the smaller channels appear to be fault-lined, and the channels are presumably down-faulted, graben. After the faulting, a great river system drained the land towards the Arctic Ocean. This river pattern was already being disrupted by river capture when the lowest parts were invaded by the sea, leaving the archipelago as we know it today. No part of the Canadian Arctic north of Parry Channel is more than 30 miles from the sea; and damp, chilling winds from the ice-filled Arctic seas in summer pervade the entire area, in striking contrast to the continental Arctic, where the summer conditions are often warm, dry, and—for a few weeks—relatively pleasant.

Farther south, faulting was closely associated with the evolution of Cumberland Sound, Frobisher Bay, and Hudson Strait, although it began earlier than the presumed Tertiary age of faulting in the archipelago.

The major physiographic elements of the North as we know it today were clearly in existence before the Quaternary. Then came the ice ages to add the finishing touches to the minor landforms and the terrain. Whether northeastern Canada already had glaciers at the close of the Tertiary, as seems to have been the case in Greenland, is not known. First and subsequent glaciations probably began on the uplands of the northeastern rim and from there spread over the north and central parts of the continent.

The Ice Age in Northern Canada

At the height of the Ice Age, almost all Arctic Canada was covered by glacier ice. Small ice-free areas included the highest mountains of the northeastern highlands, western Banks Island, and a sector of the northern Yukon, which was an eastern extension of a much larger ice-free area in the Yukon Lowlands of Alaska. About 12,500 years ago, when the maximum of the last Ice Age was past, a narrow perimeter of ice-free land had been uncovered around the margins of the Beaufort Sea. In the next 4,000 years, the northwestern margin of the ice retreated rapidly, and all Mackenzie district and the western Arctic islands were uncovered. In the east, the land was released from the ice less quickly,

and by 12,000 B.P. there was only a narrow, ice-free coastal strip; it was another 3,500 years before the eastern ice margin rapidly retreated. Already a continuous sea channel separated the surviving icecaps on the northern islands from those farther south. In the southern Arctic, where the ice sheet was still more than 1,500 miles across, it must have thinned considerably; for, between 8,000 and 7,500 B.P., the sea burst through Hudson Strait into Hudson Bay, and the ice sheet quickly disintegrated into small, rapidly diminishing remnants, in Keewatin, Baffin Island, and north-central Quebec. It was another 1,500 years before the last glacier melted west of Hudson Bay, and rather longer than this on the east and north sides.

The most spectacular influence of the glaciations on the Arctic landscape was their modification of the short, deep preglacial valleys that crossed the highlands adjacent to Baffin Bay and the Labrador Sea. At the height of the glaciations, outlet glaciers from the main ice sheet streamed through these valleys, which were over-deepened and subsequently, after the ice withdrew, submerged by the sea. Today, along the east coasts of Labrador, Baffin, Devon, and Ellesmere islands are innumerable fiords (Fig. 11-3); many have vertical walls rising directly 3,000 feet or more out of the sea to glacier-capped uplands above. The largest penetrate the highlands for more than 50 miles, and exhibit the characteristic features of the Norwegian-type fiords, with abrupt, angular changes of direction and barely submerged sills where they reach the open sea.

Ice streams do not always form classical-type fiords, even where they are flowing rapidly off interior highlands. Along several Arctic coasts—notably, the south side of Devon Island and on west Melville Island—the fiords are straight, wide in terms of their length, and probably shallow. In both areas, they have developed in horizontally bedded sedimentary rocks, and resemble the fiords of Iceland and Finnmark rather than those of western Norway.

The Pleistocene outlet glaciers were also

channelled into former river valleys that crossed the continental shelf (Fig. 11-4). These were over-deepened by the ice and now form deep gashes that are frequently stepped and often more than 1,500 feet deep on the shelf. The troughs are not visible, as they are wholly submerged; however, if the sea withdrew from the continental shelf, these deep narrow channels would be most unusual features, especially in the northwest of the archipelago. Glaciers in the Arctic mountains also created alpine scenery dominated by pyramidical peaks, glaciated U-shaped trough valleys, and cirques. Their distribution is very similar to that of the fiords, although some of the smaller forms (cirques and extended cirque valleys) are more widespread, particularly around northern Hudson Bay and Hudson Strait. The finest alpine scenery is on igneous and metamorphic rocks, and consequently is generally in the Shield.

The sedimentary rocks, whether they are horizontal-lying or deformed, do not commonly develop characteristic alpine scenery.

Although there is little doubt that glacier ice has contributed to the formation of pyramidical mountains and valley trough forms in the highlands of northeastern Canada, it is not known whether the optimum development was in interglacial times, when conditions were perhaps not unlike those that prevail today (although conceivably snowier), or during the major glaciations. At the height of the glaciations, virtually all the land surface was buried beneath ice, and the cirque-forming processes were inoperative or much reduced; if cirques were produced during the glaciations, it must have been during the onset and waning phases.

Landform modifications by glaciers were of vast importance in the mountains, but they were relatively small elsewhere in the north.

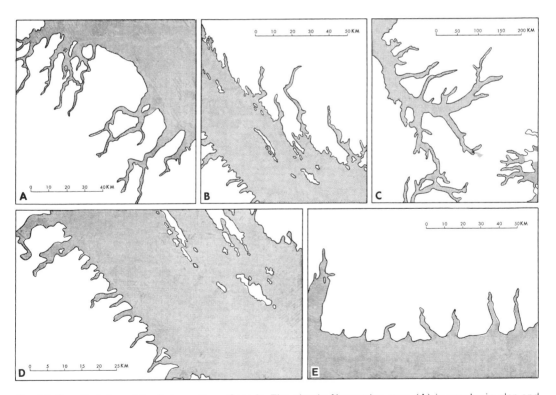

Fig. 11-3   Varieties of fiords in northern Canada. The classic Norwegian type (A) is angular in plan and about 25 miles long. Type (B) is a rectangular fiord pattern found on Baffin Island. The Nansen type fiord (C) of the northern islands is nearly 200 miles long. The cirque variety (D) and the sedimentary-rock form (E) are smaller and, in the latter case, shallow.

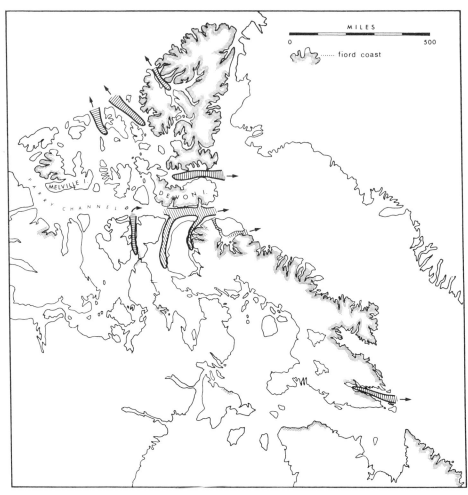

Fig. 11-4   Fiords and submerged glacial troughs. The direction of the ice movement in troughs is indicated.

This was mainly because the lower layers of the continental ice sheets were only occasionally confined by the topography, and the velocity of the ice was low. Under these conditions, erosional glacial landforms are few and restricted primarily to crystalline Shield rocks; they include glacial striae and grooves, rock bosses and low hills that show abrasion and quarrying effects by the ice, and troughs and rock basins. How far the valleys in Shield uplands, far from the continental edge, were modified by the ice is not known, as comparable studies in non-glaciated areas have not been made; but in general, the effect seems to have been small. Rock basins, today often occupied by lakes, which are numerous

in many parts of the Canadian Shield and which at first sight seem to result from uneven glacial gouging and over-deepening, rarely provide positive evidence for this on close inspection. The orientation of the rock basins is normally controlled by structure and is independent of the direction of ice flow. Many "basins" are found to be preglacial valleys plugged with glacial drift. Although there is little doubt that rock basins can be produced by glacial over-deepening, in the majority of cases they were initiated in a preglacial phase of deep weathering, and the role of the ice was to remove the weathered products. By this interpretation, the bare rock plains of northern Canada—including those west of

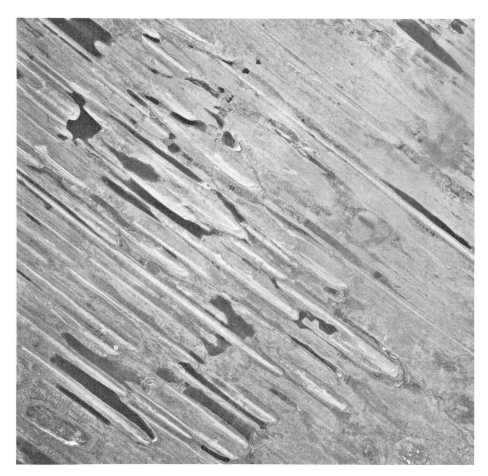

Plate 11-2   Long, thin drumlinoid till ridges that rise 15–25 feet above the Thelon River plain, N.W.T. The ice sheet that produced the ridges moved from the southeast (lower right of picture). (National Air Photo Library, Surveys and Mapping Branch, Department of Energy, Mines and Resources. Photo A14957-4.)

Hudson Bay, south of Queen Maud Gulf, in southwest Baffin Island, and elsewhere—result primarily from glacial removal of the weathered mantle, followed by minor abrasion of the larger inequalities on the exposed rock surface.

The debris that was removed from the rock plains was redeposited as till. The resulting landforms are not conspicuously different from those formed in the same way in other parts of Canada. Vast fields of drumlins and drumlinoids are preserved in the Shield lowlands between Hudson Bay and Great Slave and Athabasca lakes, and in northern Quebec. In the absence of a forest cover, they dominate the terrain when it is seen from the air;

and they control the grain of the land, even when, because of their low relief, they are not prominent on the ground. Deep till deposits are rare in the Arctic, but this is probably due to the absence of suitable parent rocks (such as clays and shales), rather than to any special properties of the Arctic environment.

Extensive till plains which show glacial patterning are not found in the northern archipelago. Drumlin fields are in fact rare within 200 miles of the northern perimeter of the Laurentide ice sheet, and are restricted to the south side of the 65° N parallel, except on Victoria, Prince of Wales, and King William islands.

End moraines were formed along the edge

of the Laurentide ice sheet, but their detailed distribution in the Arctic awaits further exploration. Preliminary observations suggest that complex belts of moraines exist on the mainland north of Great Bear Lake, and across western and northern Victoria Island. If their presence is confirmed, they will be the northern equivalent of the belts of terminal moraines on the south side of the icecap in the Midwest and in New England. Extensive end moraines, constructed during the recessional phase of the ice, are not conspicuous, except for a broken line of ridges and deposits that may be traced from the upper Back River across northern Keewatin to Melville Peninsula and subsequently to Baffin Island. This is the Cockburn moraine belt that was formed roughly 8,000 years ago, shortly before the final break-up of the Laurentide ice sheet.

As the ice sheet melted over northern Canada, great quantities of water were released which found their way eventually to the sea. In the northern islands, evidence for this phase—in the form of eskers, melt-water channels, and proglacial lakes—is limited or, on many of the Queen Elizabeth Islands, nonexistent. Farther south, within the limits of the Laurentide ice sheet, such features are more numerous. Especially noteworthy are the esker trains on the Barren Grounds (west of Hudson Bay), eastern Victoria Island, and northern Quebec. In Chapter 3, we described an esker in its simplest form, as an extended, winding ridge of fluvioglacial sediments, mainly sand and gravel, that stands about 100 feet above the surrounding land. Trunk eskers are often joined by tributary eskers; together they form a network that corresponds to the drainage pattern of the glacial rivers that once flowed in the same direction as the regional motion of the Pleistocene ice, with minor diversions resulting from the local topography.

West of Hudson Bay, the esker pattern resembles the spokes of a wheel radiating outwards from a hub south of Baker Lake. The majority of the melt-water rivers probably flowed down-slope in gorges on the surface of the icecap. If this was so, the northern eskers were developed under rather different conditions from those that formed the eskers of southern Canada, which result from rivers that flowed in or under the ice sheet.

Glacial lakes were neither as long-lived nor as extensive in northern Canada as they were in other parts of the country. Around the outer zone of the northern half of the Laurentide ice sheet, the preglacial drainage led away from the ice sheet; and as the ice retreated, the melt waters readily escaped. By the time the inner zones were deglacierized, Hudson Bay was already ice-free and drainage was towards this inner basin. In both sectors, proglacial lakes were small. A narrow lake occupied the George River Valley south of Ungava Bay, and there were shallow lakes in the middle Back River lowland and around Contwoyto Lake. The largest was in the Thelon–Dubawnt watershed of central and southern Keewatin, where the lakes were more than 700 feet deep. Unlike those in the Prairies and southern Ontario, the northern glacial lakes had only a moderate influence on the landscape. Elevated beaches and some cliffs are conspicuous in a few localities, but lacustrine sediments are not thick and do not form the wide glacial-lake plains that are such prominent features in some parts of southern Canada.

A secondary and most important effect of the Pleistocene glaciations was the extensive marine transgression of the Arctic coastal lowlands that followed them. The significance of this episode in southern Canada has been discussed already (Chapter 5); in northern Canada, its influence was even more drastic.

In Arctic Canada, south of Parry Channel, the total *postglacial* recovery of the land from the depression due to the weight of the ice varies from about 100 feet along the northwest and eastern Arctic coasts, to 500 feet in many parts of the Hudson Bay coastal lowlands and a maximum of over 900 feet on the shores of Richmond Gulf (Fig. 11-5). The transgression was not contemporaneous throughout the Arctic. The sea had withdrawn to its present position in the northwest, while the Hudson Bay Basin was still covered

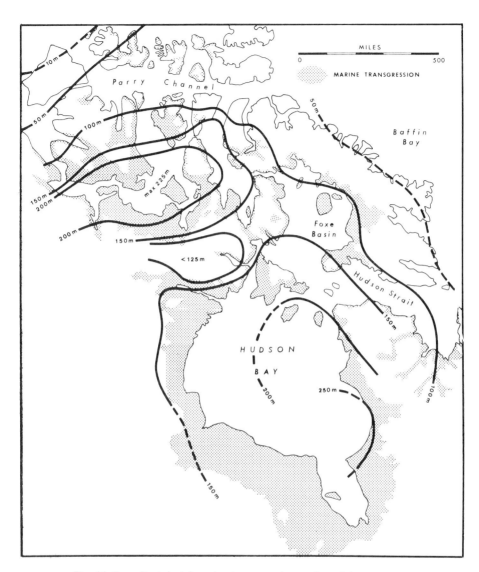

MILES
0   500

MARINE TRANSGRESSION

Parry   Channel

10 m

50 m

100 m

max 225 m

150 m
200 m

200 m

150 m

<125 m

Baffin
Bay

50 m

Foxe
Basin

Hudson Strait

150 m

HUDSON

BAY

200 m

250 m

10 m

150 m

Fig. 11-5   Postglacial marine transgression and crustal emergence

with an ice sheet and the transgression had not commenced. The marine invasion modified the lowland most strongly in three areas: (1) around the Victoria Basin—that is, in southeastern Victoria Island, northwestern Keewatin, Victoria Strait, and McClintock Channel; (2) around Foxe Basin; and (3) around Hudson Bay, where the early postglacial marine shoreline was over 300 miles *west* of Chesterfield Inlet and extended 250 miles southwest of James Bay. Hudson Bay for a brief period between 7,500 and 7,000 years ago had an area of nearly 600,000 square miles—87 per cent larger than it is today. The effect of this vast body of water on the climate of North America at the time still awaits examination.

The transgression produced few erosional landforms. At first, the land rose at 20–30 feet per century; and even when this rate had decreased, the shore retreated so quickly that there was no time for cliffs to be eroded, except in unconsolidated deposits. But constructional features are widespread. In deeper water, clays were deposited. These are often preserved today, particularly in valleys now

Plate 11-3   A limestone plateau, surrounded by elevated postglacial strand lines, overlooks an exhumed surface of the Canadian Shield: Putnam Highland and Blue Goose "Prairie", Baffin Island. (National Air Photo Library, Surveys and Mapping Branch, Department of Energy, Mines and Resources. Photo A15357-36.)

above sea level. Coarser sediments, sands and gravels, were washed into the sea by melt waters from surviving remnants of the glaciers. A most important modification was by wave action in the inshore areas, which removed the fines from the surface deposits and, as the sea continued to fall, built the residual material into beach ridges. Today these forms vary from narrow shingle ridges to broad elevated bars, 3–5 feet high and about 10 yards across, which are separated by broad lagoons or peat-filled depressions. They attain their greatest development in the

lowlands southwest of Hudson Bay, but are common through the coastal areas of the North and are especially prominent in the limestone lowlands .

Along the coasts of Baffin Bay and the Labrador Sea, the effect of the marine transgression was rather different. For a time, the land was recovering at almost the same rate as the world-wide sea level was rising through the melting of the ice sheets; as a result, the local sea level (that is, the sum of the two changes) appeared to be stationary, and a few *pronounced* beach and terrace levels were produced and later elevated above the sea. The far northern islands, beyond Parry Channel, also were depressed; but the subsequent rebound has been less than 400 feet in most areas, and in some parts less than 200 feet. The visible effect of the transgression on the scenery is not great, except around the upland coasts of the northeastern islands.

Periglacial Processes in the Arctic

As the glacier ice melted off the Arctic uplands, and the sea retreated from the lowlands, the surface of the land was exposed to other geomorphic processes. Early in this century, it was recognized that the forces acting on the Arctic landscape differ from those in more temperate latitudes. The term *periglacial* has been applied to the special northern processes in general, and particularly to those in which ice (excluding glacial ice) plays a part.

For soil moisture to survive in the form of ice for long periods, the ground temperature must remain permanently below 0°C (Fig. 11-6). This condition differs from the annual ground frost that occurs in almost all localities in winter in southern Canada and the northern United States, in that permafrost survives for at least several years, and in most places indefinitely. In northern Canada, permafrost is found everywhere beyond the treeline, except beneath the sea, large lakes, and wide rivers (Fig. 11-7). In the northern woodlands and forest-tundra zone, permafrost is generally discontinuous, with patches of unfrozen ground separating permanently frozen areas (Fig. 11-8). The southern margin of scattered islands of permafrost corresponds roughly with the northern edge of the closed boreal forest, except for sporadic patches that occur in muskeg still farther south. About a third of Canada is underlain by continuous permafrost, and in more than half the country there is a real possibility that permafrost will exist at any given site.

Permafrost varies in thickness from a few feet in the sporadic muskeg occurrences in the south, to more than 1,500 feet in the northern islands (Fig. 11-9). Deep permafrost has the effect of restricting underground drainage, but the important zone in landscape and terrain evolution is the top few feet. This is especially true of the active layer above the permafrost, which thaws every summer and which varies in depth from a few inches to several feet.

Ice accumulates in the ground under arctic conditions. In rocks, moisture enters along

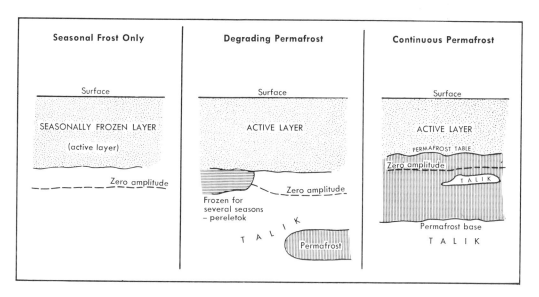

Fig. 11-6   Three varieties of frost conditions in the ground

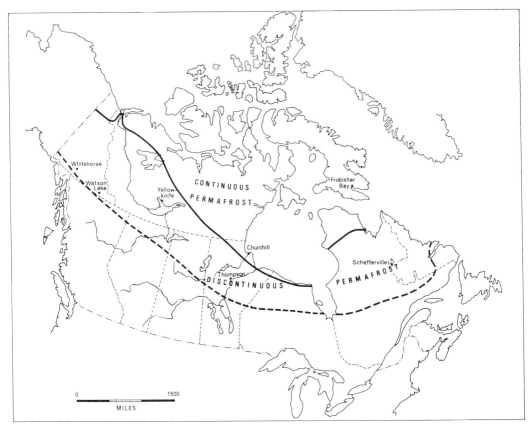

Fig. 11-7   The distribution of continuous and discontinuous permafrost

cracks, joints, and bedding planes and freezes, splitting the rock into blocks. Some rocks are more susceptible than others to this process; thin-bedded sedimentary rocks, such as sandstones and particularly the Paleozoic limestones of the interior Arctic lowlands, are rapidly broken up in this way.

In unconsolidated sediments, ice accumulates during the freeze-back in the fall. The quantity is small in sands and gravels and is rarely of major importance in clays, but it reaches considerable proportions in silts, where the ice content may exceed the amount of mineral matter in the soil. The ice may be disseminated through the soil as individual crystals, but in some localities it is concentrated into sheets, lenses, wedges, and irregular masses of clear ice. Ground ice is not normally visible, as it is buried beneath the top soil; but along the river banks and coasts

of the Beaufort Sea, where there are cliffs in the silts and fine sands, ground ice is often exposed. Nowhere in northern Canada does it reach the great thickness that is reported from the New Siberian Islands and the Lena delta, where it may exceed 200 feet; but 15 to 20 feet is not uncommon.

Ice wedges are believed to originate as thermal contraction cracks during intense winter cold; moisture migrates into the cracks and freezes, and as the process is repeated year after year, ice wedges are built up. Furrows 1–2 feet deep frequently develop above ice wedges; they intersect to produce *tundra polygons* with sides 50 feet to 100 yards across.

Under different conditions, the ground ice forms blisters or frost mounds in the soil. The most striking of these landforms are *pingos*, which are concentrated in Canada in the old

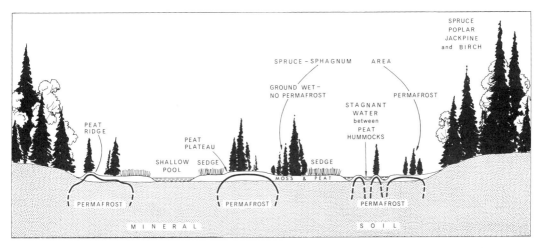

Fig. 11-8   Vegetation and permafrost relationships in Subarctic Canada (after Brown)

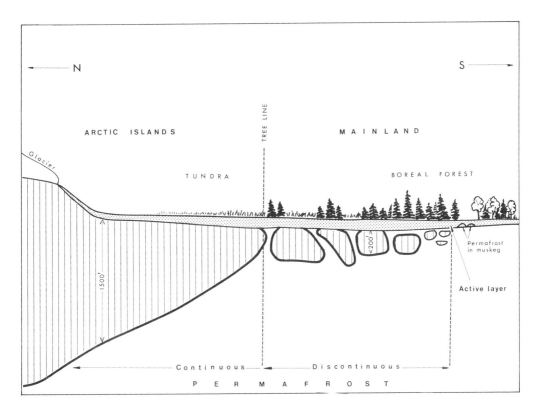

Fig. 11-9   A transect of permafrost conditions along a meridian in northwestern Canada

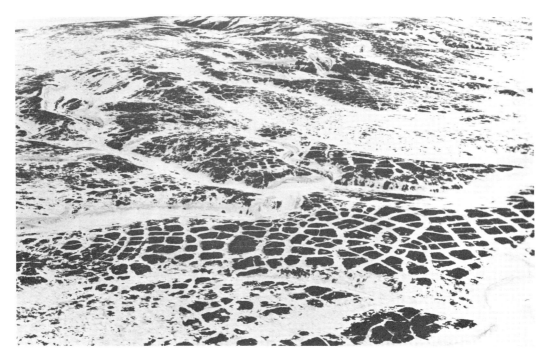

Plate 11-4   Ice-wedge fissure polygons, each about 100 feet across, emphasized by snow lying in the fissures: Ellef Ringnes Island, N.W.T. (Information Canada Photothèque. Photo by E. Bork.)

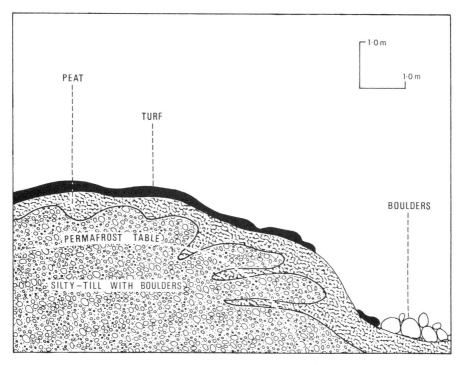

Fig. 11-10   Section of a solifluction lobe advancing across tundra

(Pleistocene) Mackenzie delta, on the east side of the contemporary delta; others of a slightly different type are found in the central Yukon. Many pingos exceed 50 feet in height, and some attain 150 feet; they are commonly 500 feet across at the base. The majority have smooth, unbroken crests, but occasionally the top is breached and ice is visible beneath the sand, silt, and organic cap. Small frost mounds are common in many parts of the Arctic where there is uneven accumulation of ice in the ground. They are also found in muskeg in the Subarctic, where peat and ice mounds are known as *palsen*.

Although the growth of ice in the ground disturbs the surface and produces hummocky terrain, even more striking features result when ground ice thaws. If the permafrost is thin, or has nearly disappeared, the water from thawing ground ice will drain away, leaving an irregular terrain with hollows several feet deep known as *thermokarst*. This type of terrain, widespread in Alaska and Siberia, is rare in northern Canada. But thaw ponds and lakes which also are initiated by thawing of ground ice are common. In its early stages, a thaw lake may be irregular in shape; but if it is in an area of homogeneous unconsolidated sediments, particularly silts, it expands as wave action and thawing pushes back the banks, and the shape of the lake comes to depend on the wind direction during the summer. When the wind blows equally from several directions, the lake assumes a circular form; but if a single direction prevails, an elongated lake develops, with the long axes *at right angles* to the wind direction.

The accumulation of ice in the ground followed by the summer thawing of the uppermost horizon leads to high moisture content in many Arctic soils, and this contributes on slopes to a slow movement downhill of the surface layers, known as *solifluction*. Slight movement may occur on slopes as low as 1°, but it is rarely conspicuous on slopes of less than 3°. The annual displacement may reach about 0.5 inches and in extreme cases 1–2 inches. In general, on the steeper slopes the velocity is higher, but this only occurs to a

point where there is failure and an earthflow develops.

Solifluction is rarely uniform across a slope, and there are zones or "streams" which show maximum velocities. In other localities, a solifluction surface may be overridden by a second sheet, and this in turn by another sheet above it. The front of a solifluction lobe or stream is often a low scarp, 3–5 feet high, in which boulders are embedded. Sections dug through the scarp reveal peat and other organic material incorporated into the solifluction lobe as it moved downhill (Fig. 11-10).

Other types of mass movement are found in the Arctic. Earthflows have already been mentioned; in the Queen Elizabeth Islands and the western Arctic generally, mud flows have been reported associated with the thawing of ground ice. In the high mountains of the Yukon, rock glaciers are a common feature. Over a hundred have been mapped in the Ogilvie and Wernecke mountains northeast of Dawson City, and they are numerous in the St. Elias Range on the Alaska–Yukon border. Rock glaciers form where there are intensely cold temperatures and a plentiful supply of rock debris, generally from rapid weathering in a cirque or on a steep mountain side. The contact between angular blocks in the talus is apparently lubricated by ice developed from moisture percolating into the debris. The blocks move relative to each other, and a "glacier" of rocks (with some included ice) moves downhill as a tongue-shaped mass that may reach half a mile in length and be as much as 150 feet thick. Active rock glaciers advance at 1–6 feet or more a year. Rather surprisingly, rock glaciers have not been identified in the eastern Arctic; it is possible, however, that boulder streams which choke the bottoms of valleys in the highland areas of the Shield, some of which appear to be moving, may be a variant of the western rock glaciers.

Other periglacial processes, not all by any means restricted to the Arctic, include the action of river, lake, and sea ice. All may be effective transporting agents, carrying debris

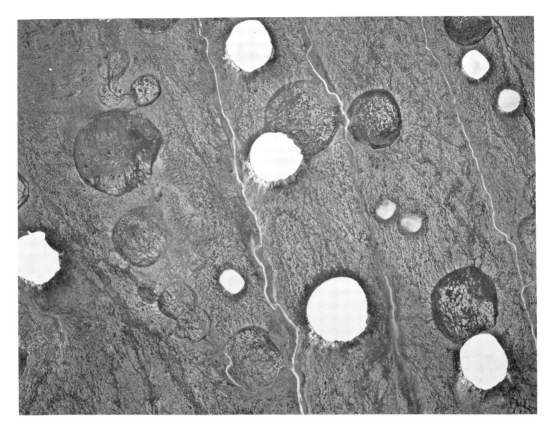

Plate 11-5   A vast wet tundra plain covered with thaw lakes (light circles) and former lakes now filled with marsh (dark circles) : the Great Plain of Koukdjuak, western Baffin Island. (National Air Photo Library, Surveys and Mapping Branch, Department of Energy, Mines and Resources. Photo A15357-71.)

that is deposited on them (from cliffs and banks) or that is picked up when ice freezes onto the bottom. A striking example is found in Foxe Basin; here, silt, stirred up from the bottom in the shallow northern part of the basin, is frozen into the sea ice and is then carried by wind and currents into Hudson Strait and Hudson Bay, where its buff colour is most conspicuous. On large lake and marine beaches, under suitable conditions, the ice pushes up massive beach ridges that are frequently 5–15 feet high. Where there is a considerable tidal range, as in the eastern Arctic, *boulder barricades*—lines of boulders developed in bays about 50 yards offshore which are awash at mid-to-high tide—are more common than beach ridges.

The wind has been considered by many field workers to be an important agent under periglacial conditions, but this must remain questionable, at least in northern Canada. The hardness of snow particles increases as the temperature drops, until at the lowest temperatures found in the Arctic feldspar minerals are abraded by blowing snow; but the results are rarely conspicuous. Wind-driven snow removes rock lichens from exposed sides of boulders, and consequently in the summer there is differential weathering between the damp, lichen-covered face that has been protected in winter and the dry, naked, rock face. The differences are usually extremely complex, and the results difficult to predict. Wind-blown dust picked up from silt deltas, outwash areas, and braided streams is found in all parts of the Arctic, particularly

Plate 11-6   Patterned ground developed by vegetation on patches of silt surrounded by sands and gravel : western Baffin Island.

Plate 11-7   A felsenmeer or boulder field formed of frost-shattered blocks of the underlying bedrock, covering an upland in the eastern Canadian Arctic.

Plate 11-8   A limestone pavement on Somerset Island, N.W.T. The surface is crossed by solution fissures and is pitted from chemical weathering beneath melting snow.

Plate 11-9   Patterned ground on an island north of Hudson Bay. One pattern is formed by a net of coarse stones that separate "circles" of finer material. A second pattern, in the "circles", results from the colonization by mosses of small pebble-filled fissures.

in the western Arctic in the spring, where brown, dust-covered snow and ice can often be traced to nearby deltas.

Snow also has a direct influence on the development of landforms. Since virtually all parts of Canada have a snow cover for part of the year, the effect of snow in the Arctic is primarily one of degree. Probably the most important modification of the landscape is indirect, through the influence of snow on the vegetation. In the southern Arctic, deep snow drifts in the spring protect shrubs and small trees from abrasion by blown snow and from wind desiccation, while later in the season they provide the soil moisture for plant growth. The double influence of a deep, protective snow bank in winter, and a plant cover that is warmer than nearby exposed tundra in the summer causes the permafrost table to retreat and the soil within the deep active layer to be less mobile than surrounding areas. If snow persists until late in the summer, however, plants fail to colonize the area, and the exposed ground is subjected to strong geomorphic action until the snow returns in September. Patches of snow that survive through several summers appear to develop basins beneath them (*nivation hollows*); several mechanisms have been suggested, including enhanced freeze-thaw action, solution, and other forms of chemical weathering, but the process is not fully understood.

Earlier we described the surface geometrical patterns in the Arctic terrain that result when ice wedges develop fissures on the surface, and these intersect to produce giant tundra polygons. Numerous other forms of patterned ground are known (Fig. 11-11). In some, the soil particles are sorted, so that the coarser material—often gravel—collects in nets, while the finer particles—sands and possibly silts—are in the centre of the nets.

Similar patterns on a large scale, perhaps four feet across, are found with gravel in the centre of circles and grading out to cobbles or boulders on the periphery. Several factors probably contribute to this type of sorting. Unequal thrusting by soil ice during the fall freeze-back on particles of different sizes is one cause; in the smaller patterns, desiccation cracking and the movement of particles into the cracks by the growth of needle ice (long, needle-shaped ice crystals) beneath the particles may be responsible.

Another class of patterned ground results from the growth of damp mobile circles in the soil. The terms *frost boils* and *mud circles* describe many of these features, which are round or oval and up to 6 feet in diameter.

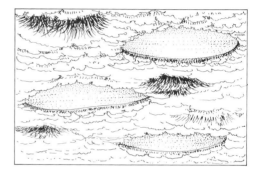

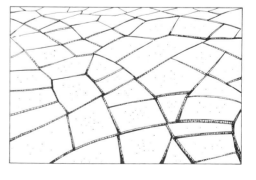

Fig. 11-11   Three types of patterned ground: a) ice-wedge fissure polygons criss-crossing wet tundra; b) circles and polygons produced by injection of fines from the sub-surface and with further sorting within the features; c) tundra or mud circles, free of vegetation and surrounded by moss tundra

In a tundra-covered terrain, they will be the only areas free of plants, as the active, mobile soil in the circle tears the roots of any plants which begin to grow. In summer, mud circles are generally wet and have often thawed when the surrounding terrain is frozen and dry.

On hill slopes, similar sorted and non-sorted patterns are found that have been pulled out by the action of gravity, into *stripes* of wet and dry, plant-covered and plant-free, coarse and fine soils.

The real importance of patterned ground is that it emphasizes the mobility of the Arctic terrain, and particularly the role of soil ice in producing geomorphic processes that are largely non-existent in the southern latitudes.

Despite the activity of Arctic soil in summer, it must be remembered that for seven to ten months of the year the ground is frozen; and consequently, in only a few places have the periglacial processes modified the post-glacial scenery to any appreciable extent. The exceptions are mainly in the western and northwestern Canadian Arctic, where there are deep silts, which are the most responsive sediments to periglacial action; and in the interior and northern Yukon, where the land was not covered by ice in the last glaciation, and the periglacial processes have therefore had tens of thousands of years to act.

In Europe, many fossil periglacial land-forms are preserved (for example, periglacial slopes, solifluction deposits, patterned ground) that were formed either south of the Pleistocene ice sheets at their maximum, or farther north as the ice retreated. Fossil features are rare in Canada. Sand wedges have been reported from the south side of the lower St. Lawrence, and fossil polygonal ground is known in the Peace River country; but there are few other examples. The periglacial processes are therefore today actively changing the landscape of the North, but in few localities—either in the past or today—have they acted sufficiently long to produce major modification in the landscape.

Selected Readings

Beals, C. S. (ed.), *Science, History and Hudson Bay*, Ottawa, Queen's Printer, 2 vols., 1968, 1057 pp.

Bird, J. B., *The Physiography of Arctic Canada*, Baltimore, The Johns Hopkins Press, 1967, 336 pp.

Dunbar, M., and K. R. Greenaway, *Arctic Canada from the Air*, Ottawa, Queen's Printer, 1956, 541 pp.

French, H. M., "Slope Asymmetry of the Beaufort Plain, Northwest Banks Island, N.W.T., Canada", *Can. Jour. Earth Sciences*, Vol. 8, 1971, pp. 717–731.

Hamelin, L.-E., and F. A. Cook, *Le Périglaciaire par l'Image*, Québec, Laval University Press, 1967, 233 pp.

Mackay, J. R., "The Mackenzie Delta Area, N.W.T.", *Geogr. Br. Memoir*, 8, 1963, 202 pp. "The Origin of Massive Icy Beds in Permafrost, Western Arctic Coast, Canada", *Can. Jour. Earth Sciences*, Vol. 8, 1971, pp. 397–422.

St.-Onge, D. A., "Nivation Landforms", *Geol. Surv. Can. Paper* 69-30, 1969, 11 pp.

Washburn, A. L., "Classification of Patterned Ground and Review of Suggested Origins", *Geol. Soc. Amer. Bull.*, Vol. 67, 1956, pp. 823–866.

12

The Hudson Bay Lowland

It was shown in Chapter 10 that several large basins have survived on the Canadian Shield since early geological times. The largest, in the centre of the Shield and nearly 1,000 miles across from north to south, is occupied by Hudson and James bays. During the Paleozoic marine transgression that covered a large part of central and eastern Canada, the central basin was filled with limestone and dolomites which buried and preserved the land surface that had existed prior to the flooding by the sea. Recent geophysical studies have shown that these rocks are preserved beneath Hudson Bay, and that in the middle of the basin they have a maximum thickness in excess of 6,000 feet. Around the margins of the bay, however, particularly on the east and west sides, the carbonate rocks have been removed by erosion, revealing the older, sub-Paleozoic surface. In Quebec on the east side of James Bay, and between Churchill and Chesterfield Inlet, the old land was exceptionally flat; and today these areas are characterized by tidal flats often several miles wide, and ill-drained, marshy terrains that slope imperceptibly towards the sea.

The limestone escaped complete denudation along the north and southwest coasts of Hudson Bay, where the plains that have developed on them are known as the Hudson Bay Lowland (Fig. 12-1). Although the geology and physiography of the two sectors are similar, the appearance of the landscapes is very different. The northern part, including the lowlands of Southampton, Coats, and Mansel islands, is in the Arctic, and the terrain is dominated by rock deserts and peat-covered tundra plains. South of Hudson Bay, widespread organic terrains—including muskeg and string bogs, Subarctic forests, and

major rivers that flow across the lowland from the Prairies and the Shield—give it a strikingly different aspect. The northern lowland has been discussed in Chapter 11 on the Arctic; the southern sector is described in the following pages.

In several parts of the basin, the underlying Shield surface is uneven, and the Precambrian rocks project through the younger sedimentaries to form low ridges and hills. At some localities, the exposures result from initial topographic irregularities on the Shield surface. The quartzite ridges on either side of the estuary of the Churchill River—on which Fort Prince of Wales, the modern town and the military camp, have been built—are apparently of this type. Far larger are the outcrops that result from structural warping along the Cape Henrietta Maria Arch that extends southwestwards from the cape of that name in northern Ontario. The arch has the effect geologically of dividing the Hudson Platform into two basins: Hudson Bay to the north, and the Moose River (and James Bay) to the south. The Hudson Bay sedimentary basin contains principally limestones and dolomites of Ordovician to Devonian age; similar rocks occur in the Moose River Basin, but here they are succeeded by non-marine Cretaceous clays, sands, and lignite, which are exposed southwest of Moosonee.

Although the Hudson Bay Lowland is predominantly flat and ill-drained, scientific exploration in the last decade has revealed a greater variety of terrain than had been suspected previously. The main discovery was the extent of the Precambrian inliers which outcrop for 150 miles in a southeasterly direction from near Winisk. For the most part, these rocks form slightly higher and

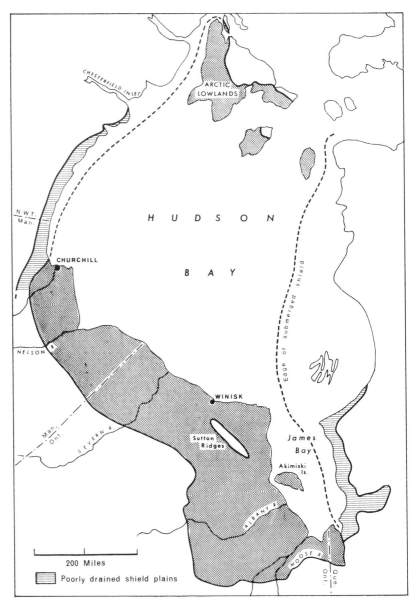

Fig. 12-1   The Hudson Bay Lowland

better-drained sections of the lowland, with occasional felsenmeer of shattered rock blocks. At the northwest end, diabase forms the top of the Precambrian series; and this results in a conspicuous ridge, the Sutton Hills, which are broken into blocks by deep, lake-filled valleys (Fig. 12-2). The steep face of the hills, partly covered with scree, is generally on the southwest side, while the upper surface dips gently towards the northeast. The sides are covered with boulder and cobble beaches formed during the postglacial marine transgression, and subsequently elevated more than 500 feet as the land recovered its preglacial altitude. The crest of the ridges reaches 900 feet and consists largely of bare rock with widely separated spruce, some birch trees, and dense arctic birch scrub.

A major part of the lowland is underlain by limestone, which slopes up gently from the

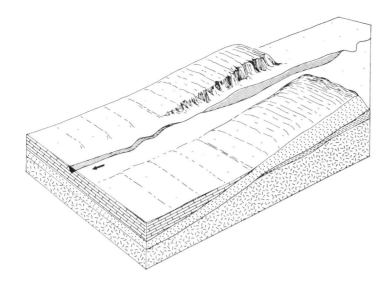

Fig. 12-2 The Sutton Ridge, northern Ontario. A dipping block of igneous and metamorphosed sedimentaries of Precambrian age overlies the crystalline basement. The Paleozoic limestones of the Hudson Bay Lowland have been removed from the ridge, and the river that flows to the left has been superimposed onto it from the former limestone cover.

shores of Hudson Bay to the edge of the Shield, where at many points it ends abruptly as a low scarp about 500 feet above sea level. Along the southwestern margin, where the limestone reaches its greatest height, the rivers flow in steep-sided valleys that cut the lowland into isolated plateaus.

At many points in the lowland, interglacial deposits—mainly fossil peat and silt, but including some marine sands and stream gravels —have been reported underlying glacial tills. Their age is uncertain, but they provide some of the clearest evidence in Canada for multiple glaciation. When the ice sheet of the last glaciation retreated from south of James Bay, a large glacial lake was created. In a short time, probably about 7,500–8,000 years ago, the ice sheet in the remainder of the lowland disintegrated as the sea invaded Hudson Bay through Hudson Strait, and rapidly almost the entire lowland area was submerged by the sea. Changes in the shape of islands in James Bay in the last two centuries and the elevation of driftwood above the high tide mark show that the land continues to recover from the depression produced by the Pleistocene ice sheet. Contemporary emergence of 1.3 feet per century is suggested by the tide gauge at Churchill.

As the sea withdrew, it left marine silts,

and lagoons trapped behind beach ridges, adding to the difficulties of drainage. Indeed, the main characteristic of the lowland during the summer is wetness. When seen from the air, the land looks as if it has risen recently out of Hudson Bay; and, especially along the James Bay coast, it is often difficult to decide where the land ends and the sea begins. The coast is extremely shallow, and at many points the tide comes in for 3 miles and more. It is not unusual for small boats to be aground without the occupants being able to see the shore.

The glacial, lacustrine, and marine sediments are frequently more than 50 feet thick, and they effectively bury the underlying bedrock. The larger rivers, especially those that flow into James Bay, are deeply cut into these sediments, and the small settlements of this part of northern Ontario are located on terraces with steep cliffs leading down to the river.

The driest part of the lowland is in the extreme south, where the boreal forest is almost continuous and where muskeg and bogs are restricted, relative to other areas. Virtually all the remainder of the lowland, amounting to more than 80 per cent, is a vast muskeg, bog, and small lake plain. Much of the area, especially near James Bay, is covered with

Plate 12-1   A pals (the light-toned, lichen-covered mound) with "drunken" black spruce : northern Ontario.

Plate 12-2   Raised marine beaches and open, Subarctic woodland on the slopes of Sutton Ridge, Hudson Bay Lowland.

string bogs in which parallel ridges of peat rise two to four feet above the adjacent surface water. Palsen and peat mounds several feet high, containing permafrost and capped with "drunken", tilted spruce trees, are widespread. Muskeg, in which the bog contains stunted black spruce and is frequently covered with shrubs, is universal; movement across them by foot in summer is exhausting and often impossible, as one sinks into the saturated moss and peat. Stands of white spruce are restricted to the better-drained soils on the slopes, where bedrock is close to the surface and in the vicinity of the rivers.

Adjacent to Hudson and James bays, the trees disappear and the terrain is either flat, undrained peat marsh, or series of gravel ridges (formerly beaches) separated by lagoons and bogs.

Selected Readings

Coombs, D. B., "The Physiographic Subdivision of the Hudson Bay Lowlands South of 60°N.", *Geog. Bull.*, No. 6, 1954, pp. 1–14.

McDonald, B. C., "Glacial and Interglacial Stratigraphy, Hudson Bay Lowland", *Geol. Surv. Can. Paper* 68-53, 1969, pp. 78–99.

Sjörs, H., "Bogs and Fens in the Hudson Bay Lowlands", *Arctic*, Vol. 12, 1959, pp. 2–19.

13

The Western Cordillera

The Western Cordillera forms a complex topographic barrier that separates the interior of continental North America from the Pacific Ocean. In Canada, the Cordillera is about 400 miles across and is neither as wide as in the continental United States, nor as high as in Alaska; the mountains, however, provide some of the most fascinating scenery in the country.

The geological history of the western mountains has already been traced in Chapter 1. From Precambrian times onwards, a complex geosyncline existed along the western margin of the Canadian Shield. It experienced many geographical changes and intermittent folding, faulting, and igneous activity. The eroded sediments from the mountains were redeposited into the geosynclinal seas and to the east over the outer zone of the Shield. The structure from the exposed Shield to the Pacific (Fig. 13-1) includes a sedimentary basin (the western Prairies), a folded and fault-thrusted belt developed in the sediments of an early part of the geosyncline (the Rock-

ies), a belt of late Precambrian and younger rocks (the Columbia Mountains—the Monashee, Purcell and Selkirk ranges), and a zone of metamorphic and igneous rocks (the Fraser Plateau and the Coast Mountains).

The major structural regions form the basis for the physiographic division of the Cordillera into three parallel systems that extend throughout western Canada from the forty-ninth parallel to the Alaska border (Fig. 13-2). The eastern system corresponds to the folded and thrust-faulted rocks adjacent to the Alberta–British Columbia border; the interior system, to the metamorphic and volcanic rocks; and the western system, principally to the great coastal granite batholiths.

The eastern system in Canada is composed of the Rocky Mountains and Rocky Mountain Trench in the south; the Mackenzie Mountains in the north-central sector; and the Richardson, British, and Brooks ranges in the far northwest. The three sectors are separated by plains and plateaus developed around the Liard and Peel rivers.

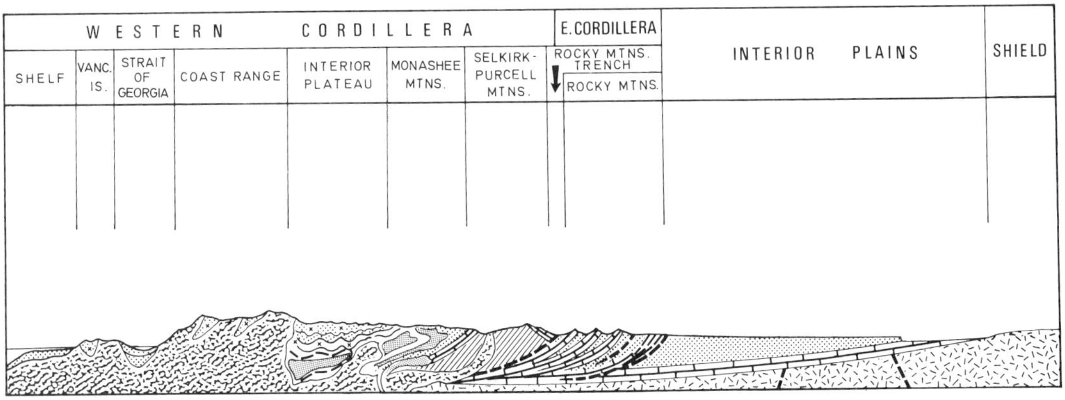

Fig. 13-1   Physiographic and geologic cross-section of western Canada from the Canadian Shield to the Pacific Ocean (after Bally, Gordy, and Stewart)

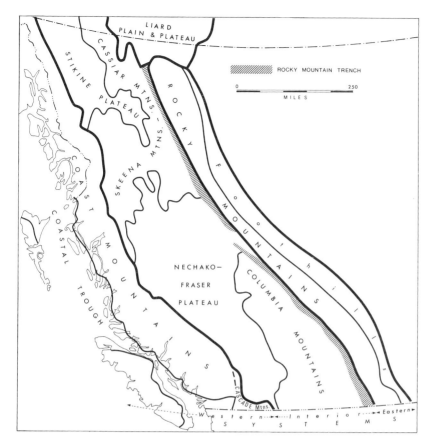

Fig. 13-2   The main physiographic regions of the Western Cordillera in British Columbia and Alberta

When the southeastern Cordillera is approached from the Alberta prairies, the first geological sign on the ground of the mountain-building events is the presence of faults that have displaced the sedimentary rocks of the plains; the more resistant beds produce the low, elongated parallel ridges of the foothills of Alberta. The fault blocks become increasingly tilted and displaced as the high front ranges of the Rockies are reached. The Rocky Mountains are composed mainly of Paleozoic limestones which were pushed eastwards over younger rocks. Today the younger rocks are generally exposed in the valleys, while limestones and quartzites form the mountains between them. The massive limestones are often strongly tilted, as can be seen in Mount Rundle near Banff. Frequently, Paleozoic and Precambrian rocks have been thrust along

faults into younger rocks; this occurs in Mount Eisenhower, where the Precambrian and Cambrian shales and quartzite that form the main mass of the mountain may be observed overlying rocks of Mesozoic age. A similar thrust has pushed the Precambrian rocks of the Lewis Range eastwards in the Waterton Lake area.

Many of the mountains in the southern Canadian Rockies reach 10,000 feet; the highest peak, Mount Robson, is nearly 13,000 feet. The scenery is not, of course, a simple result of up-thrusting of geosynclinal sediments. It results primarily from the work of the geomorphic agents, particularly running water, glaciers, and mass wasting, acting on the different rocks which have been brought together by faulting. The effect is great and often spectacular variety (Fig. 13-3). Mount

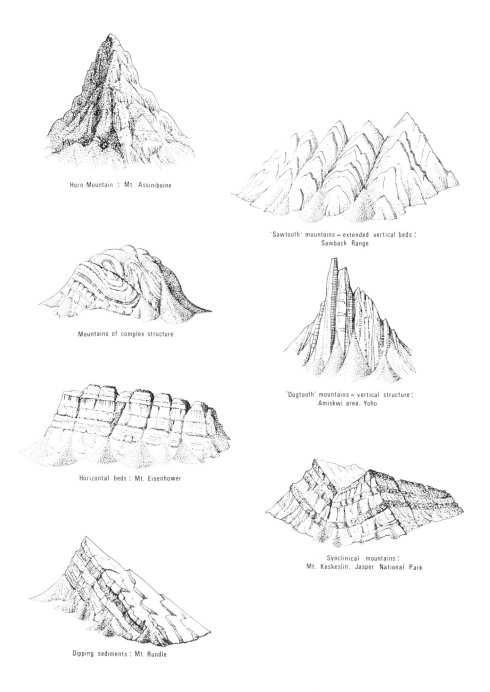

Horn Mountain : Mt. Assiniboine

'Sawtooth' mountains – extended vertical beds :
Sawback Range

Mountains of complex structure

'Dogtooth' mountains – vertical structure :
Amiskwi area, Yoho

Horizontal beds : Mt. Eisenhower

Synclinical mountains :
Mt. Keskeslin, Jasper National Park

Dipping sediments : Mt. Rundle

Fig. 13-3   Mountain forms in the Rockies (after Baird, Geological Survey of Canada)

Plate 13-1   Southern section of the Rocky Mountain Trench, near Elko, B.C. Parkland occupies
the floor of the valley and terraces line the sides.

Assiniboine has been cut into from the sides
by cirque glaciers to form a horn peak. A
repetition of minor peaks occurs where there
is one particularly resistant bed in steeply
dipping rocks, or isolated pinnacle peaks are
formed, as along the Amiskwi Valley in Yoho
Park. Other mountain shapes are found where
the rocks dip less steeply (Mount Rundle) or
are flat-lying (Mount Eisenhower).

Within the *eastern system*, and west of the
Rockies, is the Rocky Mountain Trench. This
unusually long valley is one of three trenches
occurring in the Western Cordillera, the
others being the Tintina and Shakwak
trenches in the Yukon. All three will be
described together. Characteristically, the
trenches are straight, flat-bottomed, and several miles wide and have steep, near-vertical
sides that are often 2,000–3,000 feet high.
They contain deposits of Cretaceous and
Tertiary non-marine sediments, as well as extensive Pleistocene fluvioglacial and lacustro-
glacial deposits. The Rocky Mountain Trench
extends from Flathead Lake about 120 miles
south of the Canadian border in Montana,
northwestwards for nearly 1,000 miles, until
it disappears in the Liard Plain. The floor

varies in width from 2 to more than 10 miles
and in altitude from 200–3,000 feet. It is
drained by six rivers, including the Kootenay, Columbia, Fraser, and Finlay–Parsnip
(Peace). Within the floor, isolated upland
blocks and ridges are not uncommon, and the
sides are terraced both in bedrock and surficial sediments. Two hundred miles northwest of the Liard River, the Tintina Trench
commences and extends for 450 miles, past
Dawson City into Alaska. The Shakwak
Trench, the smallest of the three, parallels the
Tintina in the southwestern Yukon; in it lies
Kluane Lake, one of the scenically most attractive lakes in Canada.

The origin of the trenches is not fully
understood. Strong structural control is suggested by the linearity of the features and the
occasional jog in their alignment. It seems
likely that the Rocky Mountain Trench (and
by analogy those in the Yukon) began as a
series of Tertiary faults, possibly graben, that
were expanded and preserved as a continuous
valley by stream action. Locally, Pleistocene
ice may have had limited erosional action,
particularly over-deepening; but the main effect of the ice was to supply the melt water

Plate 13-2   The front ranges of the Rocky Mountains seen from the western margin of the Prairies near Cardston, Alberta.

that deposited outwash material to fill the valley floor and form the contemporary terraces.

The *interior system* in its simplest form, forms a group of intermontane plateaus sandwiched between high mountain ranges to the east and west. In British Columbia, the system is physiographically rather more complex than this, for two mountain masses in addition to plateaus may be recognized within the system. The Columbia Mountains occupy a large sector in the southeast, and the Cassiar–Omineca Mountains are found in the north-central region; between the two in the southwest and centre is the large Fraser–Nechako Plateau. Smaller plateaus are close to the Yukon border.

The Columbia Mountains consist of parallel ranges—the Purcell, Selkirk, Monashee, and Cariboo mountains—with numerous peaks over 11,000 feet, that form a triangular wedge between the Rocky Mountain Trench and the Fraser Plateau. The rocks in the Columbia Mountains are principally Paleozoic and Precambrian metamorphics and sedimentaries, combined with a major granitic mass, the Nelson batholith. Orogenic activity ended in this area in the Mesozoic era (Co-

lumbian Orogeny) long before the end of mountain building in the eastern system.

The Cassiar–Omineca mountains are lower than the Columbia Mountains and have few peaks over 8,500 feet. In other ways, however, they are analogous, as they have developed principally on a granite batholith emplaced during the Columbian mountain building. They form a continuous belt of rugged mountain country west of the Rocky Mountain Trench and the Liard Plain, which separates the Nechako and Stikine–Yukon plateaus.

The Fraser–Nechako Plateau is essentially a rolling upland developed on a mixed assemblage of rocks in which intrusive and volcanic rocks of Tertiary age predominate. The plateau is narrowest and highest in the south, where it narrows to less than 30 miles between the Cascade and Monashee mountains. It is entrenched by deep valleys, including the Fraser, Thompson, and Okanagan; from the lakes and rivers in the valley bottoms, the plateau appears to be a series of low mountain ranges. Farther north, the plateau broadens, until it is 200 miles across in the Nechako–Prince George area. In this sector, it is lower, the valleys are less deeply incised, and the scenery is subdued, the general impression being one of low hills and small plains. The scenic differences between the north and south parts of the plateau are emphasized by the change in vegetation from the forests in the north to the mountain woodland, grassland, and arid sagebrush country of the south.

The *western system* includes all the land between the intermontane plateaus and the Pacific Ocean. Longitudinally, the western system is divided into three: the Coast Mountains of the mainland; the outer mountains forming the Queen Charlotte Islands and Vancouver Island; and between the two, a submerged coastal trough and associated lowlands. The most massive and highest parts are the ice-covered peaks of the Coast Mountains, which have developed on granites intruded as batholiths into the roots of the mountains during the Columbian Orogeny, and which have subsequently been exposed by denudation. The mountains have a maximum width of nearly 200 miles, and many peaks exceed 10,000 feet; the highest, Mount Waddington, is over 13,000 feet and carries ice fields covering more than 300 square miles. Farther north, the mountains form the border along the Alaska panhandle and the main St. Elias Range on the Alaska–Yukon border.

Near the United States border, south of the lower Fraser Valley, the Coast Mountains are replaced by the Cascade Mountains, which are formed on volcanic and sedimentary rocks that were later intruded by granites.

Plate 13-3   Erosional landforms ("hoodoos") in the terrace sediments that fill many of the valley floors of the Cordillera rivers: Bow River, Alberta. (Information Canada Photothèque. Photo by F. Royal.)

Plate 13-4   The valley of the Thompson River, southern B.C., was partly filled with lacustrine and fluvioglacial sediments at the close of the last glaciation. Subsequently, the sediments have been terraced as the river has cut down into them. (Information Canada Photothèque. Photo by E. Bork.)

Plate 13-5   The Fraser River, deeply entrenched into the Fraser Plateau north of Lillooet, B.C. The river is flowing in a rock gorge incised into the main valley. (Information Canada Photothèque. Photo by Gar Lunney.)

These in turn are partly overlain by Mesozoic and Tertiary sediments. Several ranges may be recognized, but none rises far above 8,000 feet.

Although the Coast Mountains are a formidable barrier to access to the interior, they are penetrated by deep, narrow valleys, several of which—such as the Skeena and Stikine—cut completely through them. The straight sectors of the valleys, joined by sharp angles that are typical of many of the valleys, suggest that they are controlled by structures in the granite. The majority of the deep preglacial valleys have been modified by glaciers into flat-bottomed troughs and fiords. Along the coast for nearly 1,500 miles from Howe Sound, close to Vancouver, to the Kenai Peninsula in Alaska there are sounds, inlets, arms, and canals—all of which are the local names for fiords. Although varying greatly in size,

they all appear to have carried glaciers during the Ice Age and to have been over-deepened, and the sides steepened by ice action. At that time, the Coast Mountains were nearly covered with huge icecaps; these formed through the accumulation of exceptionally heavy snowfalls that were produced as moist Pacific air was raised over the mountains and subjected to temperatures that were lower than they are today. Great glaciers poured off the mountain icecaps; and from interior ice sheets, ice streams passed through the existing valleys, deepening them to such an extent that when the ice melted, the sea entered the valley floors, drowning them to produce fiords.

The outer mountains of the Western Cordillera include the ranges of Vancouver and Queen Charlotte islands, part of the Alaska panhandle, and the St. Elias Range. The

Plate 13-6   A long, structurally controlled valley occupied by Isaac Lake in the Cariboo Mountains, southeast of Prince George, B.C. (British Columbia, Department of Mines and Petroleum Resources.)

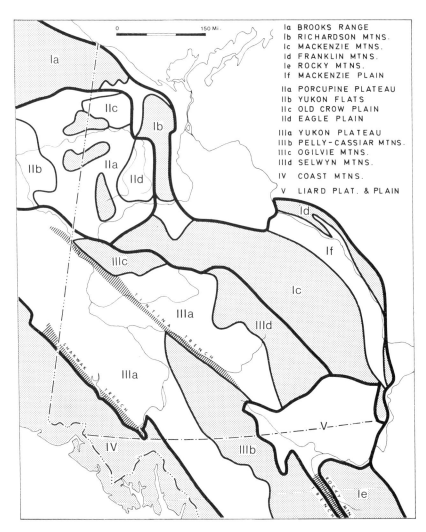

Fig. 13-4   The physiographic regions of the north Canadian sector of the Western Cordillera

Ia BROOKS RANGE
Ib RICHARDSON MTNS.
Ic MACKENZIE MTNS.
Id FRANKLIN MTNS.
Ie ROCKY MTNS.
If MACKENZIE PLAIN

IIa PORCUPINE PLATEAU
IIb YUKON FLATS
IIc OLD CROW PLAIN
IId EAGLE PLAIN

IIIa YUKON PLATEAU
IIIb PELLY-CASSIAR MTNS.
IIIc OGILVIE MTNS.
IIId SELWYN MTNS.

IV COAST MTNS.

V LIARD PLAT. & PLAIN

rocks are principally geosynclinal volcanics and sediments that were folded during several phases of the Cordilleran mountain building. Between the Coast and the Outer mountains, the depression known as the Coastal Trough is in Canada largely submerged; however, it forms the lowlands on either side of Georgia and Hecate straits and north Vancouver Island. It is not clear whether this is a structural depression, or whether it is primarily a result of erosive action on rocks that have been denuded more rapidly than the rocks in the surrounding mountains.

We have seen already that, in about 56°N,

the threefold division of the Western Cordillera is modified with the disappearance of the interior plateau. In this latitude, mountain ranges extend from the Alaska panhandle into the Skeena, Cassiar, and Omineca mountains of northern British Columbia and from there to the northern end of the Rocky Mountains. North of these mountains, the sequence from east to west of mountain range, plateau, and second mountain range reappears in northern British Columbia and Yukon Territory, although it is less simple than in the south. Here, the western system is narrower but makes up for it by its grandeur. Along the Alaska–Yukon–northwest British Columbia borders are the St. Elias Mountains, the greatest range in Canada. In the heart of the mountains are the Icefield and Fairweather ranges, which include Mount Logan at 19,850 feet. In this area, many great peaks with altitudes of over 15,000 feet penetrate through icecaps that have surfaces at 5,000–9,000 feet.

In the North, the mountains of the eastern Cordillera that correspond in position to the Rocky Mountains are the Mackenzie and associated ranges (Fig. 13-4). They are not exceptionally high, rarely exceeding 7,000 feet, and contain few glaciers today. Their ice cover was not complete or an effective agent of erosion in the Pleistocene. The mountains of the eastern system continue northwards in the Richardson and British mountains; both are composed of sedimentary rocks and appear to have escaped glaciation, except in the front ranges. North of the Rockies, the eastern system is not as continuous as it is in the south, and it contains extensive lowlands, plateaus, and plains. It is over 125 miles wide and provides a low-level entry to the interior plateaus that is in part used by the Alaska Highway. Farther north, the Peel Plateau and part of the Porcupine Plateau separate the mountains.

The northern counterparts of the Fraser–Nechako intermontane plateau are the Yukon and Porcupine plateaus. The former has an upper surface generally between 4,000 and 6,000 feet. It is deeply dissected into hill and low mountain blocks by the major rivers, including the Yukon, which flow in valleys up to 2,000 feet below the plateau. Over such a large area, there is considerable diversity in rock type, including numerous granitic intrusions and many metamorphic bodies which produce local variation in scenery. The Porcupine Plateau is more diverse than the Yukon and contains flat, ill-drained plains (such as the Old Crow flats), hills resulting from dissection of the plateau, and some mountain ranges.

From this description of the Western Cordillera, it will be evident that the present scenery had its origins in some cases as far back as Late Precambrian time, when the first mountain-building activity was developing. As with all mountains, the structural history is complex, and the various mountain-building episodes have all contributed to the evolution of the landforms. In the past million years, orogenic activity has been slight, except for limited vulcanism, which will be discussed next. But the glaciations and, in the interglacial periods, river action and mass wasting have continued to modify the landscape.

Volcanic Activity

The circum-Pacific mountain belt is currently the site of the most intense seismic and volcanic activity in the world. It is surprising, therefore, to find that neither earthquakes nor vulcanism are strongly developed in the Canadian Western Cordillera. Major earthquakes in the present century have been restricted to a narrow zone close to the coast which is believed to represent a link, deep in the crust, between the San Andreas fault zone of California and the Aleutian arc (Fig. 13-5).

There are no active volcanoes in western Canada today, although on the geological time scale we may be experiencing a temporary lull; for the Cordillera has been the site of great vulcanism in the past. The interior plateaus have been the principal area of activity—notably in the Miocene epoch, when plateau lavas, that today cover more than 15,000 square miles, flowed out from fissures to form thin, flat-lying basalt sheets from northwest of Kamloops to beyond Prince George. In the Pliocene epoch, fissure eruptions were replaced by central vents; this activity continued through the Quaternary, when there have been at least 150 active volcanoes in British Columbia and Yukon (Fig. 13-6). The majority are low cinder cones formed by a single eruption; about 90 per cent occur within two narrow·north-south belts and one east-west zone, which are presumably associated with fault belts. Twenty

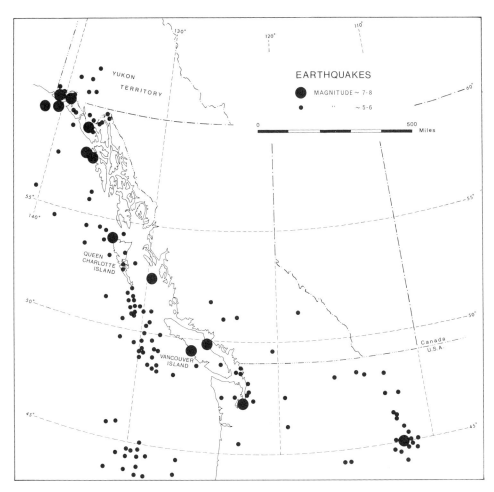

Fig. 13-5   Earthquake epicentres (between 1899 and 1963) with magnitudes of 5 and greater (after Milne et al.)

of the cones are high, composite volcanoes. Mount Edziza, 30 miles southeast of Telegraph Creek in north British Columbia, which has erupted three times in the last 1,800 years, is typical of this class.

The most recent eruption so far discovered is at Aiyanish in the Nass Range about 50 miles north of Terrace. Here, about two centuries ago, lava erupted from a vent and flowed down into the Bass Valley.

Some eruptions have been accompanied by considerable quantities of ash which have settled to the earth downwind. In Yukon Territory, several postglacial falls have been recognized from ash layers on the ground. The youngest is the White River Ash, a bilobate

deposit from two eruptions about 1,500 years ago, that covers some 125,000 square miles in the southern half of the Yukon and eastern Alaska. The source of the ash has been traced to the Klutlan Glacier area, 15 miles west of the Canadian border in the St. Elias Range.

The best known ash fall came from the caldera eruption of Mount Mazama, now Crater Lake, Oregon, about 6,600 years ago. The majority of the ash fell in the northwestern United States, but some fell in southern British Columbia, Alberta, and as far east as Medicine Hat and the Saskatchewan–Alberta border (Fig. 13-7). In the Edmonton area, two ash layers are found; the Mazama ash, which is several centimetres thick, is overlain by a thinner deposit which erupted from Mount St. Helens, Washington about 3,000 years ago. At the north end of Banff National Park, both these ashes are preserved in the soil; and there is a third, about 2,400 years old, known as Bridge River ash. It originated from a source in the Lillooet Valley near Plinth Mountain, where the ash is more than 2 feet thick.

The Ice Age in the West

The Western Cordillera supported a separate ice sheet during the Pleistocene glaciations. Although several glaciations are indicated by interglacial deposits in the Interior Plateau and particularly by the Quadra sediments of the Fraser Lowland and Vancouver Island, only the last glaciation has left sufficient evidence that the several events can be reconstructed in British Columbia. It is assumed that, when the climate deteriorated at the onset of the final glaciation, existing glaciers on the Coast Mountains and in the Rockies expanded, filling first the nearby valleys and then, as the ice accumulated, all the lower areas, until only the mountain peaks appeared through the ice. Near the sea, where the snowfall and ice accumulation must have been greatest, outlet glaciers escaped through fiords to melt in the open Pacific. East of the Rockies, glaciers descended into the Alberta foothills, where they melted or their advance was eventually stopped as they came into contact with Laurentide ice from eastern Canada. Between the two main areas of Cordilleran ice, glaciers accumulated in the intermontane plateau. During the last glaciation, the highest parts were not submerged, although they probably were in earlier glaciations. As the ice increased in depth in the interior, it was eventually able to escape to the ocean through gaps in the Coast Mountains.

The ice advance of the last glaciation

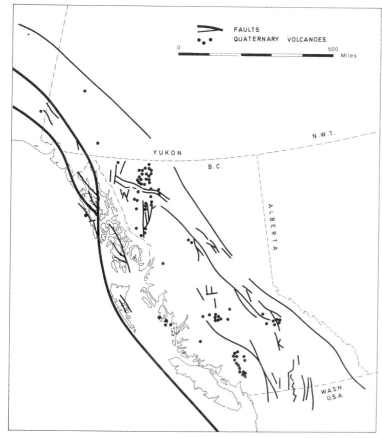

Fig. 13-6   Major earthquakes in western Canada and distribution of Quaternary volcanoes (after Souther)

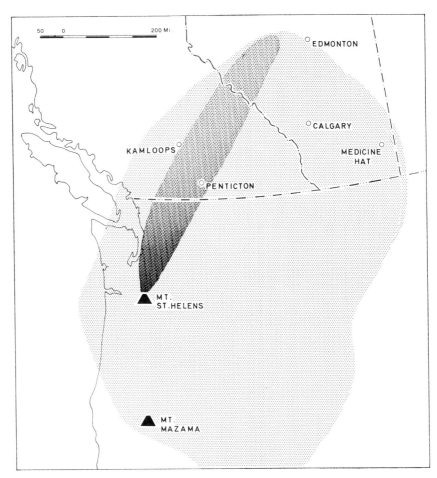

Fig. 13-7   Ash layers in western North America distributed by winds from volcanic
eruptions : Mount Mazama (light) and Mount St. Helens (dark) (after Westgate et al.)

(Fraser) reached the coast in the Vancouver region less than 25,000 years ago, and the ice continued to accumulate and extend its margins until about 15,000 B.P. Within 2,000 years, the ice front began to retreat; and a few hundred years later, much of southwestern British Columbia had been uncovered. But a fresh advance, the Sumas Stade, carried the ice forward again into the sea, covering the central Fraser Lowland about 11,000 years ago. During the subsequent retreat, a line of kame moraines was formed in the lowland between Sumas and Mission City, and also across Howe Sound.

Events in the interior of southern British Columbia are not as well documented, although the glaciers strongly influenced the

landscape. In the Purcell Trench, much of the Wisconsin period was free of ice until the glaciers accumulated in the valleys about 20,000 years ago, and this may be true of the rest of the southern interior.

It is believed that north-south valleys, controlled initially by structural features and faulting, were already entrenched 3,000–5,000 feet into the Fraser Plateau of interior British Columbia before the Pleistocene glaciations. During several ice advances, valley glaciers from the Monashee and other mountains to the east flowed into and through the valleys, excavating them further; but the amount of erosion resulting directly from ice action is not known. In extreme cases, the rock floors of the interior valleys may be below sea level; this is thought to occur at the south end of the Okanagan Valley. The glacially over-deepened troughs were filled with deposits during the several glaciations, and in places these sediments are many hundreds of feet deep. At the height of the glaciation, all of the southern sector of the interior plateau and the lower mountains (up to about 7,200 feet) were buried beneath the Cordilleran ice sheet. At the maximum, the ice generally flowed to the south and southeast, but erosion was extremely limited. In the interior, strong glacial denudation occurred, apparently during the early stages of glaciation, while the deposition of glacial, fluvioglacial, and lacustrine sediments dates from the closing phases.

Towards the close of the glaciation in the interior, ice movement became localized in each valley. Deglaciation was already well-advanced 10,000 years ago and seems to have been completed within the next 1,000–1,500 years. The higher parts of the uplands were the first to be uncovered, and shortly afterwards the ice became stagnant, with long lobes in the larger valleys and perhaps for a time active ice fields in favoured upland areas that received a heavy snowfall. Along the valley sides around the edges of the stagnating lobes, kame terraces were formed, commonly 500–1,000 feet above the valley floor and frequently sloping steeply down-valley. Many fine examples can be seen today, including some in the Fraser Valley near Lillooet. As the ice melted, the kames were no longer supported by the glaciers in the valleys, and the sediments slumped towards the valley floor. Finally, when the ice disappeared, outwash carried by the rivers from still-active glaciers elsewhere in the interior covered the bottom of the valley with sands and gravels. Occasionally, glaciers from tributary valleys surged back for a brief period into the main valley, distorting the first beds that had been deposited. In other cases, alluvial fans formed by streams from the side valleys dammed the main valley, contributing to the formation of lakes. This occurred at Penticton, where two fans join across the valley, dividing Skaha and Okanagan lakes.

The largest lakes, which were invariably short-lived, were created when the normal drainage of a valley was towards the surviving Pleistocene ice. Other glacial lakes developed even where the preglacial drainage had been away from the ice; for if the mass of the glacier was sufficient, it tilted the valley floor towards the ice, thereby permitting the accumulation of water at the ice front. Deep glacial lakes occupied the Okanagan, the middle Thompson, the Nikola, and many smaller valleys (Fig. 13-8). Deposition within the lakes complicated an already existing complex sedimentary and geomorphological record. Strand lines, beach terraces, and high level deltas—such as the massive Deadman Delta in the west end of Kamloops Lake—were formed in the lakes. Some of the terraces are constructed of silt and are particularly spectacular along the South Thompson River east of Kamloops, and locally in the Okanagan and Fraser valleys. It is not known whether they once filled the bottom of the lake or, as seems more probable, were formed when ice still occupied the middle of the lake.

When the ice retreated further, or the elevation of the land reopened old outlets, or (as in some cases) a glacial till barrier was cut through, the glacial lakes were drained and fell to occupy roughly their present positions. Landscape changes were still not complete, as the fluvioglacial and lacustrine sediments were readily attacked by flowing water, and gullies developed quickly in them. In some cases, two stages of gullies are evident. Major gullies often dissect the terraces completely, and it may be assumed that they were formed immediately after the disappearance of the lakes and ice. Within them are smaller gullies, which appear to have been formed more recently. Gulley sides are often asymmetrical, particularly when they are oriented east-west, and have a steep, vegetation-covered north face in contrast to their more gentle, arid, south-facing slopes.

Similar conditions at the close of the glaciation were also found in southeast British Columbia, in the upper Columbia, the Kootenay, and the Arrow Lakes valleys. Kame ter-

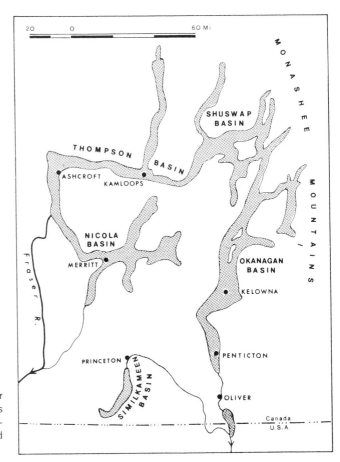

Fig. 13-8   Glacial lakes in interior British Columbia. The several basins were not necessarily filled contemporaneously. (Modified after Fulton and Nasmith.)

races and high-level glacial deposits are preserved in the eastern valleys; but in general, glacial lakes were fewer and less extensive, mainly because of the easy escape of melt waters to the south.

Glacial lakes also existed in north-central and northern British Columbia and in southern Yukon; they have been recorded from the Peace River district, the Prince George–Fort St. James region, and the Stikine Valley.

In coastal southwestern British Columbia, the land had been depressed by the weight of the ice sheet; so that, after the retreat of the ice, there was a coastal transgression by the sea. Maximum submergence was not contemporaneous throughout the area, but occurred progressively later towards the north and northeast as the ice withdrew in that direction. Emergence was extremely rapid and was more than two-thirds complete within

1,000 years. The Sumas readvance of the glacier reversed the emergence for a brief period, until, with the final retreat of the ice, crustal rebound was completed. For a period of about 3,000 years, the Fraser Lowland was about 25 feet higher than it is now before the present level was stabilized. The total emergence from the sea was about 250 feet near Victoria, and this rises to nearly 600 feet near Vancouver.

The Pleistocene in the Yukon

The Pleistocene glaciation of Yukon Territory has attracted considerable interest since it was recognized early in the present century that the placer gold deposits of the Klondike are restricted to areas that escaped glaciation. It is now clear that the northern and west-central Yukon were not glaciated, and that elsewhere the glaciation pattern is extremely complex, in terms of both chronology and source area of the ice.

During the last glaciation, the northwestern perimeter of the Laurentide ice sheet reached the borders of Yukon Territory (Fig. 13-9). The ice submerged the Franklin Mountains on the east side of the Mackenzie River but failed to penetrate far into the Mackenzie Mountains. The northern sector of the Cordilleran ice sheet covered the Pelly Mountains and the southeastern Yukon Plateau, including the site of Whitehorse. This ice originated in the Selwyn and Cassiar mountains, and its front lay from Stewart Crossing to Carmacks; within 50 miles of the edge of the ice, mountains penetrated through it at many points. Southwest of Carmacks, the interior ice was joined by ice from the St. Elias Mountains. The glaciers flowed out from massive ice fields in the range on the final occasion at least 31,000 years ago, crossed the Shakwak Trench, and penetrated the plateau hills beyond up to 5,000–6,000 feet (and rather higher in earlier glaciations), where they re-

mained until about 10,000 B.P. The Ogilvie and Wernecke mountains also supported glaciers, but they were mainly the independent valley type.

Several glaciations have been recognized in the Yukon:

Contemporary	St. Elias Range
Neoglacial	2,000 B.P. (?) – expansion of ice in St. Elias Range
McConnell	Wisconsin
Reid	Early Wisconsin (?)
Early glaciations	

The unglacierized region of the Yukon, and the even larger area of interior Alaska that escaped glaciation, are thought to be attributed to the aridity of both regions which resulted from the topographic barrier of the Alaska and St. Elias ranges to the incursion of moist Pacific air during Pleistocene time.

In the unglacierized areas at the maximum

Plate 13-7   A tor, or small residual rock knob, surviving on part of the Yukon Plateau that escaped glaciation.

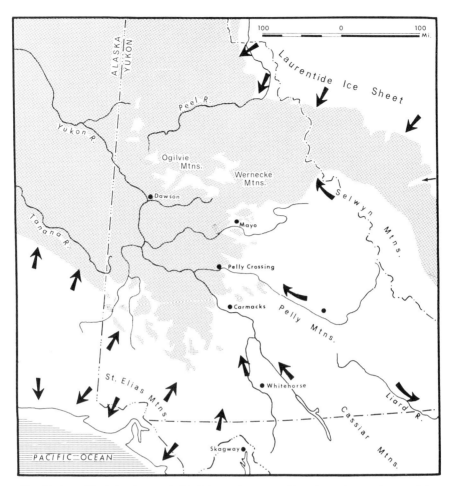

Fig. 13-9   Glacierized areas (white) in northwestern Canada at the maximum of the
last (Wisconsin) glaciation. Directions of ice flow are indicated.

of the glaciation, and during deglaciation throughout the Yukon, melt waters discharged from the ice, collected in the valleys, and eventually found their way to the sea through the Yukon drainage system. Glacial lakes were frequent, and outwash sediments were deposited in the valleys. Today these sediments underlie extensive terrace systems, such as the impressive series near Whitehorse and along the Yukon River below Carmacks. Wind-blown sediments, in the form of loess and sand dunes, were also widely distributed, particularly on the northeast side of the St. Elias Range, where outwash continues to be active today.

Early Pleistocene and Late Tertiary gravels are widespread in the non-glacierized area and probably at one time formed a surficial mantle over much of the northwest part of the Yukon Plateau. Where there was no abrasion by glaciers, the higher parts of the plateau often contain tors, rock bosses, and knobs, which produce a broken skyline. The valleys are V-shaped with linear hill-slopes, the valley floors are flat-bottomed with gravel and muck fill, and pingos are widely distributed—a combination of features that is found in no other part of Canada.

Recent Geomorphic Changes in the Mountains

The Western Cordillera, in common with other high mountain areas, shows evidence

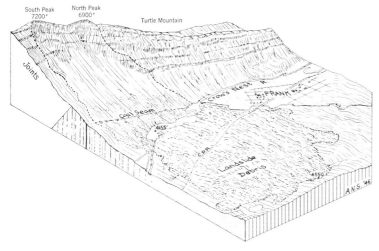

Fig. 13-10 A massive landslide at Frank, Alberta, in April 1903. The side of Turtle Mountain fell into the Crow's Nest Valley, partially blocking the river, killing 70 people in the town of Frank, and destroying the CPR line. (After Strahler, from Geological Survey of Canada.)

Plate 13-8 The site of the Turtle Mountain landslide: Frank, Alberta.

of strong contemporary geomorphic activity, and denudation is many times more rapid than in lowland areas. We have already seen that in the past, when glaciers were more extensive than today, erosion was accelerated, at least in valleys where the ice-flow was constricted between the valley sides. At present, except in the St. Elias Range, denudation directly by ice is slight, and recent major changes result from fluvial action and mass wasting.

Small rock slides are common in high mountains, as indicated by the scree slopes in many areas. Large slides are less common, but occur sufficiently often to move vast quantities of earth materials. The recurrent blocking of the railways along the Fraser Canyon and the highways in many localities is a good indication that the landscape is continually changing in the western mountains.

Two well-documented slides of major proportions have occurred in this century. At Frank, Alberta, in 1903 a mass of limestone broke away from the face of Turtle Mountain and fell nearly 3,000 feet into the valley of the Crow's Nest River (Fig. 13-10). The second major fall was from the side of the Nicolum Valley, 10 miles southwest of Hope, British Columbia, in January 1965. On this occasion, a mass of surficial and rock material, estimated to contain 15 million cubic yards, slid 4,000 feet down the valley side and spread along the valley to a depth of over 400 feet. The cause of the slide remains unknown, although it was clearly helped by the dip of the rock joints into the valley.

Selected Readings

Bostock, H. S., "Physiography of the Canadian Cordillera with Special Reference to the Area North of the 55th Parallel", *Geol. Surv. Can. Mem.* 247, 1946, 106 pp.

"Physiography and Resources of Northern Yukon", *Can. Geog. Journ.*, Vol. 63, 1961.

Fulton, R. J., "Glacial Lake History, Southern Interior Plateau, British Columbia", *Geol. Surv. Can. Paper* 69-37, 1969.

Holland, S. S., "Landforms of British Columbia, a Physiographic Outline", *Dept. Mines, Petrol. Resources Bull.* 48, 1964.

Hughes, O. L., R. B. Campbell, J. E. Muller, and J. O. Wheeler, "Glacial Limits and Flow Patterns, Yukon Territory, South of 65 degrees North Latitude", *Geol. Surv. Can. Paper* 68-34, 1969, 9 pp.

Leech, G. B., "The Rocky Mountain Trench" in "Int. Upper Mantle Symposium", *Geol. Surv. Can. Paper* 66-14, 1966.

Nasmith, H., W. H. Mathews, and G. E. Rouse, "Bridge River Ash and Some Other Recent Ash Beds in British Columbia", *Can. Jour. Earth Sciences*, Vol. 4, 1967, pp. 163–170.

Index